GW00569907

W7: Postbridge, the best known of Devon's clapper bridges

## HISTORICAL INTRODUCTION

Devon is the third largest county in England, bordering on Cornwall in the west and Dorset and Somerset in the east. It is unique in that it has two distinctly separate coastlines - north and south. The major centres of population are in the south, at Plymouth, Torbay and Exeter. Barnstaple is the largest centre in the north, but elsewhere small market towns and villages reflect a rural county.

Devon's varied geology has made for distinct regional differences. Most dominant is the high mass of Dartmoor National Park, its granite intruded into older rocks. There are Devonian shales, slates and some limestone in the south, and grits and sandstones in the far north where a portion of Exmoor National Park lies within the county. The Carboniferous 'culm measures' lie across north Devon between the two national parks. Around Exeter, Permian and Triassic sandstones give the famous red soils of Devon. Further east, there are plateau tops and escarpments of the younger Cretaceous greensands, with chalk outcropping on the coast at Beer Head. The north, generally, has poor soil whilst the richest agricultural land is in the south. This landscape has been dissected by rivers and their tributaries, many of which form long estuaries or rias on the south coast.

Devon has a mild and humid climate and is one on the wettest counties in England. The combination of fine scenery, extensive sea coasts and mild climate has made it a favoured resort for tourists and people of independent wealth from the eighteenth century to the present day.

Devon's prosperity in earlier times was based on agriculture, fishing, mining and the woollen industry. By the end of the eighteenth century, mining and the cloth industry were in decline, although copper mining was to revive spectacularly in the mid-nineteenth century.

During the nineteenth century, population increased from 340,000 to 660,000, but lack of coal for steam power and fuel curtailed industrial growth. Industrial decline and the low wages of agriculture caused significant migration to the towns and emigration overseas. Village populations often reached a peak in mid-century and some 371,000 Devonians had left their county by 1901, about one third going overseas. Plymouth's population, however, rose over fourfold and almost one third of Devon people lived in its only real industrial town and largest port in 1901. Plymouth has continued to expand in the twentieth century and light industries have halted the decline of many smaller Devon towns.

Many towns acted as markets for local agricultural produce and a number of market halls were rebuilt in the nineteenth century to provide cover from the Devon rain. The market towns and larger villages had their corn mills, maltings, tanneries and sawmills to process local produce. In the second half of the nineteenth century, dairies and creameries were added as pastoral farming increased. Brewing was once widespread in Devon but mergers and rationalisations followed national trends and the closure of Courage's brewery in Plymouth marked the end of a large-scale industry in Devon. Tuckers maltings at Newton Abbot, however, still keeps floor malting alive.

Devon's geology has been exploited by man from the earliest times. Tin streaming may have taken place on Dartmoor from the Bronze Age onwards, but for a time in the early medieval period it was the richest tin producer in Europe. From the fourteenth century until 1838, the industry came under the jurisdiction of the Stannaries with four 'coinage' towns at Ashburton, Chagford, Tavistock and Plympton. Tin was streamed and mined in open gullies or underground until 1926. Other minerals, such as copper, iron, lead and manganese, have been mined around the flanks of Dartmoor and Exmoor. Silver was mined at Bere Alston, the Teign Valley and Combe Martin. The greatest copper mine in Europe during the second half of the nineteenth century was Devon Great Consols in the important Tamar Valley mining district near Tavistock. Wolfram (tungsten) has been worked open-cast from an ore body at Hemerdon Ball.

Granite was quarried on Dartmoor and Lundy Island, slate was quarried around Kingsbridge, Plymouth and Tavistock, while Devonian limestone was worked between Plymouth and Torquay, some polished as a decorative marble. A notable freestone has been worked at Beer since Roman times. Roadstones have been quarried wherever there is suitable material. China clay has been exploited on western Dartmoor since the 1830s at Lee Moor, and deposits of ball clay are worked around Bovey Tracey and Petrockstow. Potteries, tile, pipe and brickworks developed here and elsewhere. Limekilns are found along the limestone belts and at coastal sites accessible to small trading craft. Small quantities of anthracite were once mined in north Devon, as well as lignite in the Bovey basin.

In pre-industrial times, Devon was regarded as a populous and manufacturing county, mainly on account of its extensive serge industry. The industry operated on a rural domestic basis but utilised water power in fulling mills from medieval times. Exeter acted as a finishing centre and port for cloth exports, where Tuckers Hall, a guild hall for the Company of Weavers, Tuckers (i.e. Fullers) and Shearmen of 1471, is a rare survival. Some large water-powered woollen factories - and cotton mills - were established in the county in the late-eighteenth century but few businesses survived the disruptions of the French wars and the industry declined gradually throughout the nineteenth and twentieth centuries. Machine-made lacemaking was established, however, in a failed cotton mill in the former woollen town of Tiverton. In the later nineteenth century, factories were established to produce items of clothing, such as collars and fabric gloves in the north Devon towns. Some of the builders of the early mills also established community facilities and provided housing for their workers and families. The availability of cloth waste and plentiful supplies of water for power and processing gave rise to a paper-making industry with as many as 47 mills by the 1830s. A few modern paper mills continue in business.

The sea has always played an important part in the county's economy and traditions and Devon seafarers, such as Drake, Gilbert, Hawkins and Raleigh, led the way in exploration and naval warfare in the sixteenth century during this heroic period. Before good inland communications were developed, Devon's coasts and estuaries were worked by hundreds of small sailing craft, and ports such as Dartmouth and Salcombe had fleets of schooners trading to the rest of Britain, the Mediterranean and across the Atlantic. In north Devon, Bideford, Barnstaple and Appledore were important shipping centres and shipbuilding is still carried on at the latter. Brixham was followed by Plymouth as the most important fishing port. The naval tradition was strengthened by the establishment of a dockyard at Plymouth 'Dock' (later Devonport) and this eventually became the largest naval base in western Europe. Rennie's breakwater made Plymouth Sound a good anchorage for naval and commercial fleets. Until the 1960s, transatlantic liners called here to land mails and passengers who continued to London by special boat trains.

Devon has some 8,000 miles (12,800 km) of roads, the greatest mileage of any county in England. Many were improved in the turnpike era, work which included realignments to soften gradients and

**2** rebuilding of ancient bridges. The legacy is a variety of tollhouses and some fine bridges of medieval origin, and others of the nineteenth century.

Canals were not a major feature in Devon, but the Exeter Canal was built as early as 1566. Others served local industry and agriculture, such as the Rolle (or Torrington), Grand Western Canal, Tavistock, Cann Quarry and Stover Canals. Part of the Bude Canal is in Devon.

The first steam railway was the broad gauge Bristol & Exeter, opened in 1844 and continued as the South Devon Railway to Plymouth in 1849. Here, Brunel experimented with an atmospheric railway between Exeter and Newton Abbot. The line, later part of the Great Western Railway, was converted to standard gauge in 1892. The rival London & South Western Railway from Waterloo did not reach Exeter until 1860 and Plymouth in 1890. Barnstaple was served by railways from Exeter and Taunton, and branches played an important part in the development of resorts such as Ilfracombe, Paignton, Torquay, Sidmouth and Seaton. The narrow-gauge Lynton & Barnstaple Railway was opened in 1898. There were various mineral railways on Dartmoor, serving quarries, mines and peat workings, such as the Plymouth & Dartmoor Railway, Lee Moor Tramway, Redlake Tramway, Rattlebrook peat railway and, the most unusual of the lot, the Haytor granite tramway.

Also important were developments in public utilities that sustained a growing and increasingly urban population in Devon. Part of Exeter's medieval water supply survives. Dartmoor has furnished water since at least 1591, when Sir Francis Drake was responsible for the Plymouth Leat. Two hundred years later came the Devonport Leat. Dartmoor leats, which sometimes ran for miles, also supplied water for power and dressing floors on mines. The larger towns improved supplies after cholera outbreaks in the mid-nineteenth century. As demand for water increased, reservoirs were built on Dartmoor at Trenchford and Burrator, followed in the twentieth century with dams at Ventiford, Fernworthy, Avon and Meldon. The only major dam outside Dartmoor is at Roadford, completed in 1990.

A gasworks was built in the small hamlet of Tuckenhay as early as 1806 and Exeter was one of the first provincial cities to establish works - on Exe Island - in 1815-17. As elsewhere, these works have closed in recent years. Electricity was also generated in the towns using high-speed steam engines. Larger power stations were at Plymouth and Yelland. Devon had some of the earliest hydro-electric power stations in the country, at Okehampton (1889), Lynmouth (1890) and Chagford (1891). Power is still generated at Mary Tavy (the largest HEP station in England), Chagford and Morwellham.

A number of famous engineers and inventors were born in Devon, including Savery and Newcomen (steam engine pioneers), William Cookworthy (china clay) and Charles Babbage (calculator). Devon is also associated with I K Brunel, the Rennies and John Smeaton, who all produced significant work in the county. One of Rennie's assistant's, James Green (1781-1849), established a local reputation for his bridges and canals. James Meadows Rendel was another Devon engineer of importance.

## INDUSTRIAL ARCHAEOLOGY IN DEVON

Devon had an early start in industrial archaeology when W G Hoskins outlined in *Old Devon* in 1966 the potential for the new study, and surveys of the Tamar Valley and Dartmoor appeared soon after from county-based publishers David & Charles. Much of the credit for later work rests with Walter Minchinton (1921-1996), Professor of Economic History at Exeter University 1964-1985. His 'model' county industrial archaeology guide first appeared in 1968 and he co-founded the Exeter IA Group in 1969. The first publication of the group - a guide to Exeter's IA - set a standard for others and was followed by a series of booklets on other Devon towns and IA features. Walter also organised regular IA conferences at Dartington and was one of the founders of the annual south-west regional conferences. His national study, *A Guide to IA Sites in Britain*, was published in 1984. Walter's county IA guide appeared in its fourth and final edition in 1986 and he provided the IA contribution to the second edition of Pevsner's *Devon* in 1989. This AIA guide aims to supplement Walter's work. It is also intended as a tribute to his support and promotion of the subject in Devon and elsewhere.

The authors are aware of a great number of sites and types - such as mills, cider making, agricultural industries - omitted from those selected for this short guide. However, it is hoped that this small book will inspire a renewal of interest and future investigation of Devon's industrial archaeology.

The East Devon District includes the south Devon coast from the border with Dorset at Lyme Regis to the Exe estuary in the west. It is mostly rural but a mild climate and pleasant coastal scenery provided a setting for the development of resorts at Exmouth, Seaton, and Sidmouth in the latter part of the eighteenth century. Inland there are small market towns. As with other rural districts of Devon, the buildings and engineering works of transport systems are a prominent feature of its industrial archaeology. Honiton and other villages once had a famous handmade lace industry, Ottery St Mary textile mills and Axminster has given its name to fine carpets. There are two working paper mills on the Culm at Hele and Silverton. Stone is still quarried at Beer where some of the historic underground caverns are open to the public. Other features of industrial archaeological interest include rural mills and, a rare survivor, a working oak-bark tannery at Colyton. This small town once had a foundry, four grist mills and a steam sawmill in addition to its tannery. As in other parts of Britain, the industrial archaeology of the market town presents opportunities for further research here.

### E1 AXMINSTER STATION
Axminster
SY 292982                                    ✳

The original gabled 'Gothic' station of 1859 in brick with stone dressings, now painted. The station, by Sir William Tite and Edward Clifton, is one of a series built for the L&SWR's Yeovil-Exeter extension, opened in 1860. Close to site **E2**, at Castle Hill crossing, is an early keeper's hut with a house on the opposite side of the road (SY 295987).

### E2 FORMER TEXTILE MILLS
Castle Hill, Axminster
SY 295987                                    ✳

'The Old Brush Works' is an asymmetrical block of three storeys, stone-built with brick dressings and some iron-framed windows. A small wall crane survives on the gable end facing the road. Nearby is Castle Mill, where a three-storey brick castellated block seems to have been added to a two-storey stone and brick mill.

### E3 OLD CARPET FACTORY
Silver Street, Axminster
SY 297985                                    ✳

A linked group of three-storey stone buildings with segmental-headed windows, many retaining their small panes, built after 1827 for the town's historic carpet manufacture. 'Thomas Whitty House', the name given to the end of the block furthest from the Conservative Club, commemorates the man who founded the industry in 1755. Whitty's original

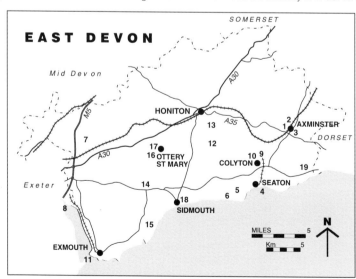

**EAST DEVON**

SOMERSET

Mid Devon

HONITON
13    A35
16 OTTERY ST MARY    12
14
Exeter    18    6    5
SIDMOUTH    4
15
8

2
1  AXMINSTER
3    DORSET

10  9
COLYTON    19
SEATON

MILES        5
Km        5

N

EXMOUTH
11

E4: Axmouth's concrete bridge

factory was burnt down in 1826-7 but the industry continued here until 1835 when the looms were taken to Wilton, near Salisbury. It was revived in the 1930s in a modern plant at Gamberlake, where carpets are still made.

### E4 AXMOUTH ROAD BRIDGE
Axmouth
SY 253899 ✳
A three-span unreinforced concrete bridge over the Axe of 50 ft (15.2 m) central span and side spans of 30ft (9.1m). It was built in 1877 as a toll bridge for the Axmouth Bridge Undertaking by Philip Brannon. The concrete has been cast to resemble classical stonework. The bridge, one of the oldest in Britain of this construction, is now a Scheduled Monument. It is in use for pedestrians, following construction of the new bridge in 1989-90. To the west is a single-storey concrete tollhouse with protruding porch and shallow barrel roof.

### E5 BEER LIMESTONE QUARRIES
Quarry Lane, Beer
SY 215894 ❑ ✳
The quarries are on both sides of the lane between Beer and Branscombe. To the south are the quarry caves, a series of substantial underground chambers where Beer freestone was mined from Roman times. The roofs are supported by pillars of unquarried stone. The last stone was removed, for repair purposes, in the 1920s. Stone was cut by hand tools, cranes being the only machinery employed. Use of Beer stone for religious buildings was widespread in medieval times, notably in Exeter Cathedral and other churches in east Devon. The quarry to the north of the road was developed after 1883 and produces stone for burning into lime in a modern kiln.

### E6 OLD BAKERY, FORGE AND MANOR MILL
Branscombe
SY 199886 NT ✳
These three sites in the dispersed settlement of Branscombe are now owned by the National Trust. The thatched, single-storey forge still works and

part of the building displays ironwork for sale. Nearby, the Old Bakery, a thatched two-storey stone and part-rendered building closed in 1987. It was the last traditional bakery in Devon and retains the oven, large wooden troughs for dough mixing and an electric mixer. A short path leads to Manor Mill and partly follows the mill leat along the base of the hillside. The small, three-storey, stone-built mill is powered by a recently restored overshot wheel with iron rim and wooden arms. The miller's house and farm buildings complete the complex.

### E7 CLISTON MANOR WINDMILL TOWER
Broadclyst
SX 991966 ☆
A red sandstone tapered tower, 30 ft (9.1 m) high and 14 ft (4.2 m) internal diameter at its base. According to the inscription on the tower, the mill was built in 1786. It was disused by 1815 and later converted for housing. A modern roof has been fitted.

### E8 FISHERS BRIDGE MILLS
Clyst St George
SX 971882 ✳
A former tidemill with later steam mill, at the eastern end of the eighteenth-century Clyst Bridge. The two-storey tide mill is rendered with a slate roof. The adjacent three-storey steam mill, dated 1911, is in red brick with pale brick dressings. Traces of leats can be seen alongside the now embanked river but the mill pool has been filled. The mill worked until 1960 and is now used in the supply of animal feed. The wheel and machinery have been removed.

### E9 COLYTON STATION
Kingsdon, Colyton
SY 252941 ❑
A two-storey station house with single-storey offices in red brick with yellow and black decorative details in Italianate style. The platform survives. The

E6: The Forge, Branscombe

5

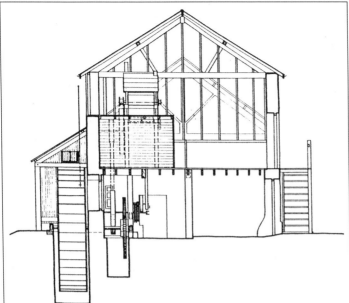

E12: Poltimore Farm wheel and thresher
*Drawing: Martin Watts reproduced by Courtesy of English Heritage*

station served the Seaton Junction-Seaton branch, opened by the Seaton & Beer Railway in 1868, later to be absorbed by the L&SWR, and closed in 1967. Part of the route is now used by vintage reduced-scale electric trams of the 3-mile (4.8 km) Seaton Tramway.

## E10 THE TANNERY
King Street, Colyton
SY 243942 ■ ✳

J & F J Baker & Co's oak-bark tannery consists of three-storey buildings in rubble stone with wooden boards and louvres on the upper floors. The buildings date from the eighteenth and nineteenth centuries. One of only two such concerns to operate traditional processes, the tannery produces leather for soles, saddlery and harness. The tannery also dresses or curries the leather with traditional oils and hand tools to produce bridle, stirrup and harness leathers. The tannery has a leather shop.

## E11 EXMOUTH DOCKS
Exmouth
SX 994807 ✳

Prior to the opening of the docks, Exmouth was a fishing port and base for pilot boats for the Exe estuary. From 1750, the town developed as a resort. A square basin with entrance channel, the dock was built 1865-68 in a hollow on the Point and reconstructed in 1882 to provide an accessible and safe alternative to tidal Topsham and Exeter or a voyage up the Exeter Canal. The docks closed in 1990 and are currently used for fishing and pleasure craft, while new housing surrounds part of the basin. The former Docks Co's Offices and Custom House are located on the approach from the Esplanade.

## E12 POLTIMORE FARM MILL
Farway
SY 176970 ✳

A recently restored water-powered farm threshing mill in a remote setting in the valley of the Coly. The mill building is part of an irregular quadrangle of buildings which include a medieval house. An overshot wheel of 14ft 7in (4.4m) diameter of 1846 (by J Maunder of Ottery) drives threshing machinery and is supplied by a pond on the east side of the Poltimore road.

E13: Copper House tollhouse, Honiton

**6**

## E13 COPPER HOUSE TOLLHOUSE
Axminster Road, Honiton
ST 172005                                    ✳

A distinctive castellated tollhouse of the Honiton Trust with rounded front, tall pointed windows and front porch. Its ornamental iron toll gates are now set back from either side of the widened road. Another Honiton Trust house of two storeys with protruding five-sided front can be seen at Turks Head (ST 149001) near the junction of the A30 and Honiton by-pass.

## E14 TOLLHOUSE
Newton Poppleford
SY 079895                                    ✳

Situated at the junction of the Exeter-Sidmouth and Budleigh Salterton roads. A small, rectangular, single-storey, thatched cottage of two bays with pointed windows, believed to have been built in 1758 and therefore the oldest in Devon. The road was the responsibility of the Lyme Regis Trust.

## E15 OTTERTON MILL
Otterton
SY 079852                                    ❑

A working nineteenth-century corn mill powered by a leat from the River Otter on a site used as such since medieval times. The present stone-built mill is of two storeys with attics and four bays. It ceased to grind in 1959 but was subsequently restored by a trust and started milling again in 1979. The mill has two wheels by Bodley Bros of Exeter and three surviving pairs of stones including two French burrs

dated 1859 and 1862. It is open to the public and has display material relating to its restoration. The mill house is across the road.

## E16 ST SAVIOUR'S BRIDGE
Ottery St Mary
SY 094951                                    ✳

A single-span road bridge of 1851 over the River Otter. The road surface is supported by five cast-iron ribs of 83 ft (25.3 m) span. A cast-iron plate at the centre of the arch records the construction date and supplier (Joseph Butler & Co's Stanningley Ironworks near Leeds). The bridge, built to replace an earlier structure, was widened in 1992 and provided with a new deck with additional parapets inside the original ironwork.

## E17 TEXTILE, CORN MILL AND TUMBLING WEIR
Mill Street, Ottery St Mary
SY 095953                                    ✳

The complex next to St Saviour's Bridge has three sites of interest. The five-storey brick serge mill, of sixteen by five bays, was built in 1788 by John Duntze and George Yonge to revive the failing woollen trade of the area. However, by 1823 it had become a silk factory and was later used for a number of businesses. The mill once had the largest waterwheel in England. Immediately to the east is the Town Mill, in brick, with miller's house. This corn mill was closely associated with the textile mill, being built by Duntze & Yonge in 1788-90 to replace the earlier Town Grist Mills. A 'tumbling weir' was

E17: The tumbling weir at Ottery St Mary

**7**

E18: Tollhouse and tollgate, Sidmouth

built in the middle of the mill leat to take water not required to drive the mills via a tunnel into the River Otter. The mills, weir and St Saviour's Bridge can be viewed in a short 'circular' walk.

## E18 SIDMOUTH BRIDGE TOLLHOUSE AND TOLLGATE
Sidmouth
SY 129878 ✳

A single-storey tollhouse on the Salcombe Regis road, in 'Greek Revival' style with prominent porch and central tall, tapered chimneys (c1817). The house has been restored by the Sid Vale Association. The old tollgate (c1820) has been restored and hung next to the tollhouse at the entrance to a riverside walk. Another tollhouse survives in Station Road (SY 123875), as does the former railway station in Bulverton Road (SY 121886).

## E19 CANNINGTON VIADUCT
Uplyme
SY 317924 ✳

A ten-arched mass-concrete viaduct designed by A C Pain, and built in 1903 with the aid of an overhead cableway, to carry the Axminster to Lyme Regis Light Railway. Owing to settlement, the third arch on the western side of the 92-ft (28 m) high viaduct has been reinforced with two brick arches built within the concrete structure. The line closed in 1965.

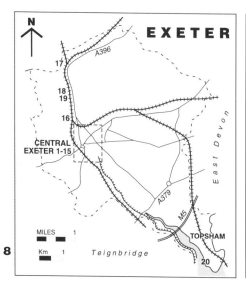

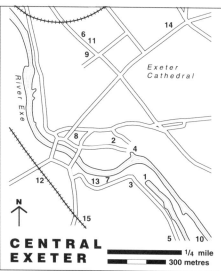

The Exeter City Council District includes the city, its suburbs and the port of Topsham. Sited on high ground above the lowest crossing point of the Exe, Exeter has been a regional and route centre since Roman times. One of the leading towns in Britain in the early eighteenth century, competition from the north diminished its role in the once-important woollen industry and its nineteenth-century industrial base included paper mills, tanneries, foundries, breweries, corn mills and maltings. Exeter's industrial archaeology includes some remains of these industries, together with substantial reminders of the improvements in transport and public utilities of the industrial era.

## EX1 CITY BASIN AND EXETER CANAL
Haven Road
SX 921918                                            ✱

James Green's Exeter Canal (1825-30) terminates in this 18-ft (5.5 m) deep basin, surrounded by fine stone warehouses. The canal originated in 1564-6 as a 1³⁄₄-mile (2.8 km) canal to by-pass weirs that had prevented ships reaching the river quay in Exeter. The first in England to use the pound lock, it was extended downstream in 1675 and enlarged in 1701. From 1825, Green extended the canal 2 miles (3.2 km) to an entrance lock at Turf (SX 964861). This new basin was opened in 1830. The basin and warehouses, which were added later, recently hosted the Exeter Maritime Museum. A short branch from the South Devon's main line was opened in 1867 to the basin and the base of a wagon turntable, now restored, survives with broad and narrow gauge track.

## EX2 CRICKLEPIT MILL AND LOWER MILLS AREA
Commercial Road
SX 918921                                            ✱

The area between Commercial Road and the medieval city walls to the east of the Bishop Blaize Inn has been partially cleared for development. The site is traversed by the medieval Higher (extant) and Lower (culverted) leats that once powered at least five corn or cloth mills here, some subsequently converted to other industrial uses. Cricklepit Mill, a brick and stone corn mill, survives close to the inn. The building contains a 13-ft (4 m) diameter undershot wheel from the nineteenth century and another external wheel. A decayed undershot wheel of Lower Mills survives in the midst of the cleared area. Nearby, supported by scaffolding, is a former corn mill (known as Edge Mill or Quay Mills) dated 1824 which was later used for grinding barytes.

EX6: North Street iron bridge, Exeter

**9**

The Dryhouse dates from the seventeenth century, when the woollen industry was at the height of its prosperity. Timber-framed on brick piers, it was formerly open on both sides to allow the air to dry cloth, stretched on tenter hooks (which survive) after fulling at the nearby mills.

### EX3 ELECTRICITY GENERATING STATION

Haven Road
SX 920918
*
A large ornate generating hall in red brick with pale brick dressings, built in 1896 and closed in 1960. The entrance bay is decorated with a coat of arms and the ornamental front of the building includes relief panels depicting the spirits of electricity. The tall stack has been demolished.

### EX4 EXETER QUAY AREA

SX 920921
*
The River Quay is sited near the former Water Gate of the walled city and has probably served as a landing place for small craft from Roman times. A stone quay and crane had been built by 1567 and subsequent additions represent growth up to the late nineteenth century when Exeter's trade began to decline. The principal sites include:

The Quay House, currently a visitor centre, built in 1680-81 as a transit shed and covered quay. An excavated lighter dock can be seen here. The Custom House dates from 1680-81, the first major brick building in the city. Recently restored, the oldest custom house in Britain has particularly fine ornamental plaster ceilings. Opposite, the small wharfinger's or harbourmaster's office of 1778 has an attractive weathervane and curved parapet. The two five-storey warehouses dominating the quay were built in 1835. The first is in white limestone with red stone dressings. The other is of sandstone with stone and brick dressings. The two bonded stores at the start of Commercial Road are both named and dated. The first, in grey stone, was built

EX3: Haven Banks generating station, Exeter

EX4: Custom House, Exeter

**10**

EX4: Warehouses and the fishmarket, Exeter

for the wine merchant Samuel Jones in 1878 and the other, in brick, for Kennaway & Co in 1892. The open ironwork structure of the late nineteenth-century fishmarket now houses the cast-iron King's Beam, formerly used in weighing dutiable goods. The beam of 1838 was cast by A & W C Bodley, whose iron foundry was nearby until its closure in 1967.

## EX5 GAS WORKS
Haven Road
SX 923916                                    ✷
The works of the Exeter Commercial Gas Light and Coke Company, established in 1836. The boundary wall, the office building at its entrance and some stone and brick buildings (one dated 1867) at the north-east corner of the site are partial survivals of this large works. It was the last in the South-West to make gas from coal when production ceased in May 1971.

## EX6 IRON BRIDGE
North Street
SX 917927                                    ✷
Erected in 1834-6 for the city's improvement commissioners and the Exeter Turnpike Trust. The viaduct comprises masonry approaches, some arched, with a cast-iron bridge supported by six 40 ft (12.2 m) spans with attractive spandrels with the name of the makers, Russell & Brown's Blaina Iron Works. A smaller iron bridge of 1814 carries a footpath over the Cathedral Close (SX 922925).

## EX7 THE MALTHOUSE
Haven Banks
SX 917919                                    ❏
This substantial stone and brick building of three storeys, now converted into a pub and restaurant, was latterly in use as a maltings, as is evident from the three pyramid-shaped kiln roofs across the centre of the block. The original building, identifiable by the distinctive curved wall nearest the Exe, was built as a brewery c1789, with a malthouse added shortly after. Brewing finished when the business was taken over by the nearby City Brewery in 1833. The building was used as a maltings, with extensions and rebuilding in the second half of the last century. Malting ceased in 1949. It then served as a bonded warehouse for St Anne's Well Brewery.

## EX8 MEDIEVAL EXE BRIDGE
SX 916922                                    ✷
The present twin bridges over the Exe (1968 and 1972) replaced an ornamental steel structure of 1905 which had in turn replaced a masonry bridge of 1778. The construction of the new bridges and demolition of the former City Brewery has exposed $8\frac{1}{2}$ arches of the thirteenth-century Exe Bridge. One of Britain's earliest surviving bridge works, the arches are now set in the landscaped area between the new works. The bridge has both semi-circular and pointed, or Gothic, arches and is built primarily of local volcanic rock from Thorverton and Ide. It is thought the original bridge was about 650 ft (200 m) long with 17 or 18 arches as it crossed marshland in addition to the main river channel. The ruins of St Edmund's Church are integral with the last two arches of the bridge.

## EX9 THE OLD MALTHOUSE
Bartholemew Street East
SX 917926                                    ✷
A fine former maltings of the nearby St Anne's Well Brewery. Built into the steep slope above the

**11**

EX11: St Anne's Well Brewery, Exeter

Longbrook Valley, it is thought that parts date from the sixteenth century. A circular kiln, by King's of Nailsworth, adjoins the rectangular malt barn. Malting ceased in 1966 and the building has been converted for restaurant use.

## EX10 PAPER MILL
Trews Weir
SX 925916 ☆

A two-storey stone and brick mill, now converted into housing, with date stone of 1780. It probably incorporates a cotton mill that was eventually converted to papermaking in 1835, a trade that continued until 1982. The weir was built by John Trew in the 1560s to provide sufficient depth of water for his canal, and the potential for water power was subsequently exploited by fulling mills.

## EX11 ST ANNE'S WELL BREWERY
Lower North Street
SX 917927 ✳

Recently restored for multiple use, including a pub and micro-brewery, the former brewery is one of the most impressive of Exeter's industrial monuments. The complex retains the brewhouse of 1878 (nearest the city centre) and extensions of c1886 beside the viaduct. The site, built on a steep slope, was served by a railway siding from the L & SWR's goods yard to the rear. Malting and brewing seem to have started on the site from 1820 and were latterly carried on by Harding Richards & Thomas's St Anne's Well Brewery Company Ltd of 1889. This firm was acquired by the rival City Brewery of Norman & Pring in 1944 and subsequently passed to Whitbread (1962). Brewing ceased in 1968.

## EX12 ST THOMAS STATION AND VIADUCT
Cowick Street
SX 915919 and SX 916917 to SX914920 ✳

The station and fine classical entrance building was built in 1846 for the South Devon Railway. Currently an unmanned halt, it kept its overall roof until 1970. The St Thomas Viaduct is almost one-third mile (0.5 km) in length and has 62 arches. It was built of random coursed rubble with brick voussoirs to carry the single track of Brunel's atmospheric railway. A second viaduct was added in 1861 when the line was doubled.

## EX13 TANNERY
Haven Road
SX 917919 ✳

The most significant structure of this former tannery is a stone warehouse with a large double doorway to the road. The tan and lime pits were sited to the west of this warehouse, as were the drying lofts and hide house. The tannery had been established by 1798 and it is thought that the warehouse forms part of a later extension. It was used as a bark store and for drying hides. Tanning ceased in 1896 and the building awaits redevelopment.

## EX14 THE UNDERGROUND PASSAGES
SX 926935 to SX 923928 ❑

A series of man-made tunnels beneath central Exeter which provided access to the city's major piped water supply from medieval times to the early nineteenth century. The first passages were constructed in the fourteenth century with extensions in the next century. The Exeter tunnels are notable for their extent, size and accessibility and are, in the main, lined with stone.

## EX15 WELL PARK BREWERY

Willeys Avenue
SX 917916  *
This former brewery is sited a short distance from the end of the St Thomas Viaduct. It dates from c1870 and has a tall central block, flanked by symmetrical wings of three bays in red brick with yellow brick trim. Originally the brewery of Stevens, Pidsley & Co, it was eventually acquired by J A Devenish & Co Ltd of Weymouth in 1925.

## EX16 ST DAVID'S STATION

Bonhay Road
SX 911933  *
The present stone-faced facade of the station dates from a GWR rebuild in 1911-4. To the rear are island platforms. The station was originally built in 1844 for Brunel's Bristol & Exeter Railway. It was rebuilt (by Henry Lloyd and Francis Fox) in 1864 as a glass and iron-roofed station of 132 ft (40.2 m) span between stone side walls. The GWR block was built in front of the 1864 facade, some of which can be seen to the rear, identifiable by tall round-headed windows.

## EX17 COWLEY BRIDGE AND TOLLHOUSE

Cowley
SX 907955  *
A three-span ashlar structure with fine architectural detail of 1814 by James Green, Devon's first county bridge surveyor. To the east, near the junction of the Crediton and Tiverton roads, is a small single-storey tollhouse.

## EX18 EXWICK MILLS

Exwick
SX 907940  *
A substantial mill on the Exe in dark red brick with pale brick dressings. The four-storey main block is of six bays with four bays and gable end to the road. Rebuilt in 1886 on the site of the Higher Woollen Mills, the mill worked until 1958. It was powered by a large Poncelet wheel, now removed, by Taylor & Bodley of Exeter. Part of this former flour mill is now in retail use.

## EX19 EXWICK TOLLHOUSE

Station Road, Exwick
SX 908936  *
A relatively unaltered single-storey brick and slated house of the Exeter Trust. The central bay, which is extended from the front of the house, has the main door with a rectangular recess for a board above. The house was built in 1858 and commanded two gates.

## EX20 TOWN QUAY

Topsham
SX 967877  ❏
*
The present quay was built over older landing places by the L&SWR when a branch line from Exeter was opened here. The quay was extended 80 ft (24.4 m) into the river joining the old Town Quay with Steamer Quay to the south. Relics of maritime activity include the eighteenth-century King's Beam, for weighing goods (see Exeter Quay), the Lighter Inn (formerly the customs house, then harbourmaster's office and workshops) and a number of two-storey stone warehouses, most now converted for retail/domestic use. The line of the railway, removed in 1958, follows Holman Way and retains an iron over bridge. The area to the north and south of the quay has much of maritime interest, especially **Topsham Museum** at 25 The Strand.

The Mid Devon District extends from the Taw Valley in the west to the Somerset border near Hemyock in the east, and from the outskirts of Exeter in the south to the fringes of Exmoor in the north. It is traversed by important transport routes - the Bristol-Exeter (former GWR) mainline, the M5 motorway and the North Devon Link Road (A361). The valley of the River Exe runs through the district. It is now mainly agricultural and quite remote in its western parts. Tiverton was once the centre of an important woollen industry and is the district's largest town. Others include Crediton, an ancient ecclesiastical centre, Bampton and Cullompton. As with the industrial archaeology of the other rural districts, transport features are prominent and include a restored branch of the Grand Western Canal. The Culm valley had an important textile industry and some mills from its later declining stages survive. Tiverton's textile mills became a centre for machine-made lace and there are significant remains of John Heathcoat's factory settlement here. Otherwise, some corn mills survive in the villages and market towns, as do the buildings of a small brewery at Uffculme and a maltings in Crediton. Limestone is worked for roadstone at Westleigh, Burlescombe.

## M1 MILL, MALTHOUSE AND TOLLHOUSE
Bampton
SS 959222 and SS 960221                    ✳

The ancient market, fair and woollen town of Bampton was on the main North Devon-Taunton road, now effectively by-passed by the motorway link. The town is built from local stone and has a number of interesting features within a short distance of the 1827 bridge over the River Bathern. To the rear of New Buildings, the Town Mill (SS 959222) is now converted to housing, but retains the waterwheel (by C. Davey & Sons, 1910) and launder. The line of the leat is indicated by stone slabs laid across the lane. The 'Toll House' (SS 960221), a square two-storey, two-bay stone building of the

Tiverton Trust, is at the junction of the old and new (c1825) Tiverton roads, the latter following the river valley. Next to the bridge is 'The Old Malthouse' (SS 959222), a low stone building that has also served as a brewery and workhouse. Bampton's limestone quarries are now largely worked out. A number of the old quarries are sited either side of the old Tiverton road, a little to the east of the old tollhouse, such as Kersdown Quarry (SS 962223).

## M2 EGGESFORD STATION
Chawleigh
SX 682115                                   ✳

A large stone station house and offices with gables, bay windows and a coat of arms. The buildings are now a private dwelling, but the platforms - arranged to accommodate the attractive riverside

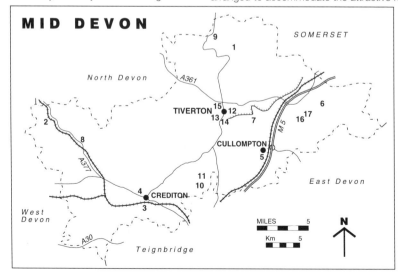

**MID DEVON**

14

location - are still in use on the Exeter-Barnstaple line.

## M3 CREDITON STATION
Crediton
SX 840995　　　　　　　　　　✳

A rare example of a GWR-style station on a L&SWR route, the outcome of the competitive strategies of the early companies. The attractive small station house has bays to either side and is built in brick with stone dressings. The platform awning survives. It was constructed in 1851 for the broad-gauge Exeter & Crediton Railway, possibly to Brunel's design and is currently under conversion for residential use. The line was later operated by the L&SWR, whose small signal box and footbridge (1878) survive near the level crossing.

## M4 MALTHOUSE
Penton Lane, Crediton
SS 837004　　　　　　　　　　✳

'The Maltings' are two joined, long, low, rendered-cob and thatched buildings, converted to housing in 1984. Four projecting bays are situated on the side opposite the lane. Malting, leatherworking and milling were significant industries in this former woollen town, as suggested by street and building names.

## M5 CORN MILLS AND LEAT
Cullompton
ST 024077 to ST 024070　　　　✳

Cullompton once had a number of corn mills powered by a substantial mill leat from the River Culm that runs to the east of the town's High and Fore Streets. This can be followed by a public footpath. The three-storey Higher Mill (ST 024077) has been converted to housing but a water turbine remains. Little survives of Middle Mill (ST 024074), its name commemorated by the lane which meets the footpath here. The corner of this brick-built mill and a tunnel entrance to the leat can still be seen. Lower Mill (ST 024070) was the last mill to work, until 1968, and is now the most complete. The three-storey building over the leat is now in residential use but the sluices by Stenner & Gunn of the Lowman Ironworks, Tiverton, are still in use.

## M6 TEXTILE MILL
Culmstock
ST 103139　　　　　　　　　　✳

A three-storey rubble-built main block with an L-shaped extension in brick and stone. It was built in 1877-8 to replace an earlier mill and was water-powered until the 1920s. It is now converted to residential use - 'The Old Mill' - but retains its large lowbreast/undershot wheel (by Bishop Bros of

M6: Culmstock Textile Mill

Wellington) at the eastern end, together with the embanked leat and sluices.

## M7 CANAL AQUEDUCT
Halberton
SS 997122　　　　　　　　　　✳

Brunel's aqueduct was built to carry the Grand Western Canal over the branch railway from Tiverton Junction to Tiverton in 1848. The aqueduct has an iron trough supported by two brick arches. It was relined by butyl rubber in 1976 to prevent water damage to the brickwork.

## M8 LAPFORD MILL
Lapford
SS 732079　　　　　　　　　　❑

A three-storey corn mill with nearby mill house served by a leat from the River Yeo. The house was built c1430 and the mill reconstructed in 1887 following a fire. In 1995 the iron breastshot wheel was restored and run again.

M8: Lapford Mill

**15**

M13: Heathcoat's mill and school, Tiverton

## M9 EXBRIDGE TOLLHOUSE
Morebath
SS 933242                                    ✳
A distinctive octagonal tollhouse of the Minehead Trust, with circular central chimney, sited on an 'island' at the crossroads of the A396 and B3222.

## M10 THORVERTON BRIDGE
Thorverton
SS 936016                                    ✳
An early single-span reinforced-concrete bridge over the Exe which was opened to road traffic in 1908. The deck is carried by four reinforced-concrete ribs of 84 ft (25.6 m) span and the bridge has ball finials at each end of the parapets.

## M11 THORVERTON CORN MILL
Thorverton
SS 935017                                    ☆
A substantial four-storey stone mill with segmental-headed windows and red brick dressings. The double ranges were built in 1898 and are now surrounded and dwarfed by modern storage and processing units. The mill was closed by Allied Mills in 1989 and the machinery removed. The mill was served by the Exe Valley Railway which ran nearby.

## M12 CANAL BASIN
Canal Hill, Tiverton
SS 963124                                    ❏
The basin, embanked on its northern side, of the Grand Western Canal. John Rennie's canal was constructed from this basin to the summit level at Lowdwells (ST 073196) 7³/4 miles (12.5 km) away as a contour canal in 1810-14. It was extended by James Green, as a tub-boat canal, in 1838 but this section was closed in 1867. The part of the canal from Burlescombe to the basin remained in use for stone traffic until 1924. The canal to Lowdwells is now a linear park. At the basin, the embankment has a number of limekilns. Two (of 14 in 1842) have been restored with a small interpretive display.

## M13 HEATHCOAT'S MILL AND WORKERS' HOUSING
Leat Street, Tiverton
SS 952128                                    ✳
The main five-storey brick-built lace factory dates only from 1936 after a fire had destroyed earlier premises. The site, powered by a leat from the Exe, began as a cotton mill in 1792. This was taken over by John Heathcoat of Loughborough and partners for bobbin-net making in 1816. The only surviving buildings from c1816 are the classical gateway lodges. Tiverton Museum has a Heathcoat Lace Gallery which includes early prints, samples of lace and a bobbin-net machine from the factory. Of greater historic interest is the workers' housing in nearby Heathcoat Square. Two rows of three-storey blocks face each other across gardens. These consisted of flats for single workers above two-storey houses. Near the main entrance is an ornate school of 1841 for educating the children of factory operatives by day and operatives by night. Later factory housing has been added in the adjacent streets such as Seymour, Alexandra, Victoria and Elm Terraces and John, Church and Melbourne Streets. The name 'Loughborough' is commemorated in early housing by the mill leat to the north of the factory. William Burges's Knightshayes Court was built for Sir John Heathcoat in 1873. It is now a National Trust property (SS 960152).

## M14 TIVERTON MUSEUM AND PRESERVED LOCOMOTIVE

St Andrew Street, Tiverton
SS 955124 ❑

A former GWR class 1400 Collett 0-4-2T locomotive, similar to those that once worked the Exe Valley railway, preserved here with many railway relics from the area. Other museum exhibits include two iron waterwheels by local engineers Nott & Cornish, the wooden gear for a horsemill and many agricultural implements and vehicles by local firms.

## M15 TOLLHOUSE

Bampton Road, Tiverton
SS 952137 ✻

A two-storey rendered house of the Tiverton Trust with ornamental barge-boards. It is sited on part of the old road immediately south of the roundabout at the junction of the A396 and new A361 motorway link road. A similar tollhouse of this trust survives on Longdrag in Tiverton at the junction of the old roads to South Molton and Witheridge at SS 947132. A wooden toll gate with side gate for pedestrians of the Tiverton Trust is on display in Tiverton Museum.

## M16 COLDHARBOUR TEXTILE MILL

Uffculme
ST 062122 ❑

Buildings from the eighteenth to the twentieth centuries survive here. The centre-piece is the three-storey 'fireproof' brick and stone mill built by Thomas Fox in 1799. Fox, a woollen manufacturer of nearby Wellington, had purchased a grist mill here for the water power potential of the site. The mill closed in 1981 but was reopened as a working museum by the Coldharbour Mill Trust in 1982. The present breastshot wheel, 18 ft x 14 ft (5.5 m x 4.3 m), was installed in 1897. Steam power had been added in 1865 when production changed from earlier serge and flannel to worsteds. The surviving Pollit & Wigzell horizontal cross-compound engine of 1910 replaced two earlier beam engines. An 1867 Kittow & Brotherhood beam engine has been restored to working order. The boiler house contains Lancashire boilers, one of 1888, and nearby is the octagonal brick chimney. Cottages built for rent to workers survive nearby in this factory community, an example of the Quaker philanthropy of the Fox brothers.

## M17 FURZE'S BREWERY

High Street, Uffculme
ST 069129 ✻

A long, narrow, four-storey building of nine bays in red brick with stone dressings. An octagonal tower, with blind windows to the top storey and a date stone **WDAF 1838**, forms the eastern end of the block. The brewery was taken over by rivals Starkey, Knight & Ford Ltd of Bridgwater in 1918 and is now a warehouse. It is quite unlike other surviving brewery buildings.

M16: Coldharbour Mill, Uffculme

The North Devon District includes most of north Devon's seaside resorts but is mainly rural and sparsely populated. The scenery is varied and hilly, rising to include part of Exmoor and its National Park in the east. The main resorts grew significantly in the Victorian era but previously served as market towns and harbours, as did Barnstaple, the largest town in the district. North Devon's once-important woollen industry declined at the turn of the nineteenth century but a variety of industries have left their traces on the landscape. Many existed to serve local agriculture, such as limeburning, and to process its products in tanyards, corn mills, sawmills and maltings. In addition, potteries, textiles and furniture-making have been locally significant. Coastal shipping was historically important in north Devon and Barnstaple became a route centre for turnpike roads and railways. Most of these railways have now closed, including the narrow-gauge Lynton & Barnstaple line. The Lynton Cliff Railway is, however, still open.

## N1 BARNSTAPLE TOWN STATION

Castle Street, Barnstaple
SS 556332                                                                      ✲

Opened in 1898 as a joint station for the Ilfracombe line and the newly-opened Lynton & Barnstaple Railway. Stone-built with ashlar dressings, this station replaced an earlier 'town' station near Queen Anne's Walk. The L&BR closed in 1935 and the station in 1970 when services to Ilfracombe were withdrawn. The station buildings and platform awning have been retained in a redevelopment of the site, as has the signal box. A plaque on one of the new residential blocks commemorates the L&BR.

## N2 DERBY LACE FACTORY

Vicarage Street, Barnstaple
SS 562336                                                                      ■

This factory, once one of three lace plants in the town, was opened in 1825 by John Boden, a former partner of John Heathcoat of Tiverton. The 12-bay brick block was originally of four storeys and had an attractive cupola. It is of fireproof construction and was powered by steam. Extensions were added in the late nineteenth century to accommodate modern machinery. All but three bays of the top storey have been removed, following a fire in 1972. Opposite, the Yeo Valley Primary School was Alfred H Miller's evening institute for his employees, as indicated on the foundation stone of 1900. The 'Derby' area around the factory was formerly occupied by terrace housing, built to accommodate the mill workers. Lace was last made in 1970 but synthetic fibres are still knitted here.

## N3 ELECTRICITY GENERATING STATION

Castle Street, Barnstaple
SS 556332                                                                      ✲

Built in 1903 with an extension of 1937. The red brick building to the rear of the site, now partly demolished, housed the original reciprocating steam plant, later supplemented by diesel sets. The station closed in the 1950s and has been partly

ILFRACOMBE

LYNTON

Exmoor

SOMERSET

N

BARNSTAPLE
1-11

Exmoor

SOUTH
MOLTON

Torridge

Mid Devon

MILES 5

Km 5

**NORTH DEVON**

redeveloped. The office blocks on Castle Street remain the best evidence of former use.

## N4 GLOVE FACTORY
Pilton, Barnstaple
SS 556342 ✻
One of the few remaining relics of a once extensive leather industry, this tall rubble-built glove factory on the lane leading to Pilton church was closed in 1970. Fashion gloves from lamb and sheep skins were made here from c1860, replacing earlier manufacture of rougher agricultural gloves.

## N5 LITCHDON STREET POTTERY
Barnstaple
SS 560329 ✻
The elaborate showrooms and part of the work-rooms of the former pottery date from 1886 and feature red and cream brickwork with terracotta panels. One of the bottle kilns has been relocated to the rear of the Brannam Medical Centre. This historic pottery site was until recently the works of C H Brannam Ltd. Using the local red Fremington clay, Brannams have produced a range of every-day ware, from flowerpots to clay ovens, and, from the late nineteenth century, art pottery. Royal patronage was obtained, thus 'Royal Barum (i.e. Barnstaple) Ware'. Brannams were taken over in 1979 and the new owners have relocated to a modern factory at Roundswell where they keep a museum. The Litchdon pottery has been redeveloped. Displays of Barum Ware and other pottery artefacts are displayed in the **Museum of North Devon** on The Square.

## N6 LONG BRIDGE
Barnstaple
SS 558329 ✻
This historic bridge has 16 pointed arches and was originally joined by a causeway on either side, the

N5: Litchdon Street Pottery, Barnstaple
*Photo: Marilyn Palmer*

River Taw being half a mile (0.8 km) wide at high tide. Of medieval origin, it was widened in 1796 and 1832-4, latterly by James Green. Its present appearance dates from 1963 when it was widened on the upstream side only. The medieval width of the bridge can be seen in the pedestrian subway on the 'town' side of the bridge. Traffic is now lighter due to the opening of the new Taw crossing.

N7: Barnstaple Pannier Market
*Photo: Marilyn Palmer*

## N7 MARKET HOUSE AND BUTCHERS' ROW

Off High Street, Barnstaple
SS 559332 □
A covered market hall of 1855-6, 320 ft (97.5 m) long with a glass and timber roof supported by iron columns. Alongside is Butchers' Row, a street flanked by one-storey shops or stalls for the town's butchers. This complex formed part of a block bounded by the Guildhall of 1826 and a corn exchange of 1864. At the junction of High Street and Butchers' Row is a granite quoin, dated 1879, showing the centre-point for local turnpike mileage.

## N8 QUEEN ANNE'S WALK

The Strand, Barnstaple
SS 557331 ✳
This single stone colonnade probably dates from the late seventeenth century. It was rebuilt and the statue of Queen Anne added in 1708. It originally served as a merchants' exchange and faced the town's quays. The seventeenth-century Tome Stone, where money could be placed when closing a sale, was put in the colonnade in 1900. The town's quays were filled when the Barnstaple-Ilfracombe railway was built in 1874, and their facilities were replaced by the reconstructed Castle Quay to the west of the walk.

N12: Chelfham viaduct of the Lynton & Barnstaple Railway

## N9 RALEIGH CABINET WORKS

Bridge End Wharf, Barnstaple
SS 556329 ☆
Built after 1888 by Shapland & Petter as a group of separate blocks, predominantly in pale Marland brick with red brick dressings. Two blocks of seven bays face the river but some in front of these have recently been demolished. The works were named after their former site at Raleigh, where new technology from the USA was applied to the manufacture of quality furniture by this firm. The flow of production in this new steam-powered complex began with a sawmill, adjacent to the Long Bridge and proceeded through separate blocks, planned to minimise the risk of widespread fire damage, as had occurred at the original Raleigh works. The site was formerly Westacott's shipyard.

## N10 RALEIGH TUCKING MILL

Raleigh Meadow, Barnstaple
SS 564340 ✳
Situated on the old mill leat which carried water from higher up the Yeo valley to Barnstaple Town Mills, now surrounded by modern housing, this painted rubble mill building retains the iron shaft of its waterwheel. Its history is obscure, a corn mill is referred to in deeds of 1699 but the name suggests it once worked in the finishing stages of North Devon's woollen industry. Nearby is the site of a late eighteenth-century factory settlement. Workers' housing, opposite on Higher Raleigh Road survives (SS 564341).

N
↑
Pilton
4
10
11
2
7
1
3
8
6
9
5

● Barnstaple
Station

MILE                    1/2

Km              1

**BARNSTAPLE**

## N11 SANDERS' SHEEPSKIN SHOP
Pilton Causeway, Barnstaple
SS 556336 ❑
This fellmongery business moved here in 1869, the firm having been established by John & Samuel Sanders in 1844. The processes are traditional but modern machinery is now employed. To the north-east were the offices, depot and yard, of the Lynton & Barnstaple Railway. The entrance gateway for the railway survives at the fellmongery.

## N12 CHELFHAM VIADUCT
Chelfham
SS 610357 ✳
A substantial yellow-brick viaduct on masonry piers, 400 ft (121.6 m) long and 70 ft (21.3m) high, for the narrow-gauge Lynton & Barnstaple Railway. With eight arches of 24 ft (7.3 m) span, it is the largest brick viaduct constructed for a narrow-gauge line in Britain. It was designed by F W Chanter.

## N13 KNAP DOWN SILVER-LEAD MINE
Combe Martin
SS 596466 ☆ ✳
A ruined engine house and chimney are the most visible remnant of seven centuries of silver-lead mining in the Combe Martin area. A Sims compound pumping engine was installed here in 1843 and was still in working order in the 1890s after the mine had closed. In Combe Martin, a former smelt mill building is incorporated in Loverings Garage, Borough Road (SS 577471).

## N14 BICCLESCOMBE MILL
Ilfracombe
SS 518465 ❑
An eighteenth-century mill, rebuilt in the 1960s and restored by Ilfracombe Rotary Club in the 1970s. The mill has an overshot cast-iron wheel 17 ft (5.2 m) diameter on the gable end. The two-storey building at Bicclescombe Park now hosts the Old Mill Cafe.

## N15 HELE MILL
Ilfracombe
SS 536476 ❑
A small stone-built farm mill, rebuilt in the eighteenth century but originally of the sixteenth century. It has been restored with machinery from North Molton Mill, and is the only working flour mill in North Devon. The mill has an 18 ft (5.5 m) diameter cast-iron waterwheel by Garnish & Lemon of Barnstaple.

## N16 ILFRACOMBE HARBOUR
SS 525477 ✳

Ilfracombe is now North Devon's largest resort but was from medieval times, a market town, fishing harbour and commercial port. The holiday trade dates from the 1770s with major development from Victorian times. The old pier, probably of medieval origin, was extended (1760) and rebuilt (1824-9) by the local landowner. Opposite is the site of the last commercial quay and former shipbuilding yard. To the west is The Quay, now faced by guesthouses. The promenade pier was added after 1873 to accommodate Bristol Channel steamer traffic, its wooden structure being replaced by concrete components in 1952. St Nicholas Chapel, on Lantern Hill, served as a lighthouse in the sixteenth century. Below Lantern Hill is the old lifeboat house of 1866.

## N17 WINDMILL STUMP
Instow
SS 482312 ✳
Walls c10 ft (3 m) high survive of this 12-ft (3.7 m) diameter windmill tower on a hill above the village near the church. Another windmill and a tidemill, near Instow Quay, once worked in this small resort.

## N18 LYNMOUTH HARBOUR
Lynmouth
SS 723496 ✳
Originally built in the eighteenth century for the herring fishery, with a Rhenish tower added in the next century. Former limekilns (SS 722496), now a shelter, can be seen close to the lower station of the cliff railway.

*right* N19: Lynton & Lynmouth cliff railway

N25: Heddon's Mouth limekiln, Trentishoe

## N19 LYNTON CLIFF RAILWAY
Lynton and Lynmouth
SS 720496                                          ☐
A working railway carrying passengers up the cliff (gradient 1 in 1³/₄) from the seaside at Lynmouth to Lynton, 430 ft (131 m) above. Two cars are linked by wire rope and 700 gallons of river water, released by the bottom car, provides the ballast for the system. Opened in 1890, the railway was designed by George Marks, built by Robert Jones and financed by the publisher Sir George Newnes. It was originally intended to carry freight brought by sea to the harbour below, but is now a major tourist attraction.

## N20 BREMLEY AND GOURT MINES
Molland
SS 818283 and SS 820283                            ✳
Deposits of iron and copper were found in close proximity at Bremley and Gourt mines, the two possibly being connected underground. Remains of large pits (Danes Pits) can be seen to the left of the farm gate at Bremley Cross. To the east, are the course of a leat, spoil tips and the remains of a small engine house of 1857 at Gourt Mine. Mining began here in the seventeenth century and copper was produced until 1867 and iron to 1894.

## N21 BAMPFYLDE MINE
North Molton
SS 737327                                          ✳
Iron and copper were mined in North Molton from medieval times. Bampfylde Mine, worked on either side of the River Mole, produced copper, iron and manganese before closure in 1877. The extensive site is now covered by a forestry plantation. Re-

mains include a crusher house once worked by a 30-ft (9 m) waterwheel (SS 732326). Accessible evidence of mining can be seen to the left of the road through Mines Wood at SS 738327 where there is an adit into the rock, just north of a large tip.

## N22 FLORENCE MINE
North Molton
SS 751320                                       ☆ ■
Lead, copper and iron were mined here until 1885. New Florence Iron Mine was the most productive in the area and was reopened during both world wars. The remains of shafts, adits, buildings and machinery survive in the valley on the end of South Wood. The mine was linked by a 4-mile (6.4 km) tramway to the Taunton-Barnstaple railway in 1874.

## N23 WOODY BAY STATION
Parracombe
SS 683464                                          ✳
A stone-built chalet-style station typical of the Lynton & Barnstaple Railway. It was built at remote Martinhoe Cross for a planned resort at Woody Bay, which never developed. The station was purchased in 1995 by an association planning to rebuild part of the line and open a museum here. Other L&BR stations are at Blackmoor Gate (SS 645431) and Lynton (SS 719488).

## N24 MOLE MILL AND LOWER MILL
South Molton
SS 723259 and SS 723257                            ✳
Mole Mill is an attractive two-storey woollen mill in stone with slate roof and bell turret on a seventeenth-century site. There is an extension to the east or riverside. The waterwheel and leat have not survived. To the south of Mole Bridge is Lower Mill, a three-storey woollen mill last used as a grist mill to the mid-1950s. The overshot wheel has been removed and the leat filled. These mills, both now domestic accommodation, are rare survivals of the area's woollen trade. Nearby is a tollhouse (SS 725258).

## N25 HEDDON'S MOUTH LIMEKILN
Trentishoe
SS 655496                                      NT ✳
A small circular kiln in an exposed position above this landing place, that has been damaged by storms. The kiln is of drystone construction with a single pot. Two pointed arches provided access to the working areas. A small display on the lime trade can be seen in the National Trust's shop at Hunter's Inn. Similar small coastal kilns remain at Woody Bay (SS 676492) and Lee Bay (SS 694495).

Plymouth, Stonehouse and Devonport were known as the Three Towns until their amalgamation in 1914. Industrial archaeology here has a dominant maritime flavour, covering harbours around the mouths of the Plym and Tamar. The latter has important crossings to Cornwall and is also home to the great naval base at Devonport (Plymouth Dock until 1824). The Victorians built a ring of forts to defend the dockyard, many surviving as at Crownhill, Bovisand, Drake's Island and the Breakwater. There are connections with notable civil engineers: John Smeaton's Eddystone lighthouse, John Rennie's long breakwater and the magnificent Royal William Yard, James Rendel's Saltash and Torpoint chain ferries, while I K Brunel's influence is seen at Millbay Docks and the Royal Albert Bridge. The Plymouth and Devonport Leats from Dartmoor were significant early water supply works, the first being associated with Sir Francis Drake (see West Devon **W5**). The Plymouth & Dartmoor Railway was opened in 1823-6, but contact with the rest of England came with the South Devon Railway after 1849; the London & South Western Railway approached Plymouth from the west 41 years later. All these lines had branches to the docks. Plymouth was much bombed in the Second World War.

## P1 CATTEDOWN QUARRIES
SX 492536                                                    ✳

Former limestone quarries at Cattedown and Prince Rock now accommodate a variety of industries and oil tanks, their extent being a good indication of how much stone was removed. Cattedown Wharves on the Plym opened in 1888. Opposite are boat repair yards at Turnchapel and Oreston. Now an industrial estate, Oreston's Breakwater Quarry (SX 503538) supplied stone to Plymouth Breakwater. Today, the industry is dominated by large limestone quarries and a cement works across Laira Bridge at SX 510542,

## P2 COATES GIN DISTILLERY
Southside Street
SX 481542                                                    ❏

In Plymouth's Barbican area, Coates & Co's dry gin distillery was established in 1793 in part of a fifteenth-century Dominican friary (later, a debtor's prison). Historic equipment from the 1850s includes two pot stills and a steam pump by Shears & Sons of London. The distillery is open for guided tours.

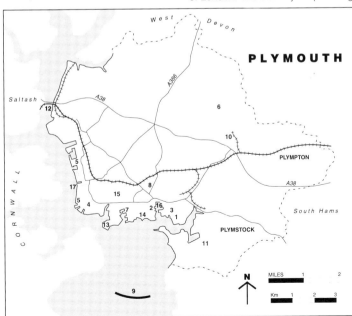

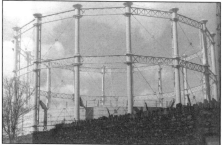
P3: Gasholder at Coxside, Plymouth

## P3 COXSIDE GASHOLDERS
Coxside
SX 491540 ✳

A gasworks was established here in 1842 but was later replaced by a larger works at Oreston. There is a major redevelopment underway just below the remaining gas holders of three types: guided by cast-iron columns, a lattice frame and a large spiral-guided type.

## P4 DEVONPORT MONUMENT
Ker Street
SX 454544 ✳

Tall column of Dartmoor granite erected to commemorate the changing of Devonport's name from Plymouth Dock by royal decree in 1824. Here are also the classical Town Hall and Egyptian style Oddfellows Hall, designed by local architect John Foulston. They survive in an area largely destroyed by Second World War bombing.

## P5 DEVONPORT ROYAL DOCKYARD
Devonport
SX 452540 to SX 440572 ❏ ■

The royal dockyard was founded in 1691 by William III at Plymouth Dock. It now extends along a 2-mile (3.2 km) shore of the Hamoaze. Despite wartime bombing, several listed buildings and other struc-

P5: The East Ropery, South Yard, Devonport
*Photo: Plymouth Naval Base Museum*

P4: Devonport monument and Town Hall

tures survive in the historic South Yard. There were two 1,200-ft (366 m) long roperies, with associated stores of 1776. The East Ropery, rebuilt after a fire and missing its north end, is a three-storey fire-proofed building with iron frames and stone floors. The cellars remain of the bombed West Ropery. Four adjacent store houses survive, as does the Joiners' Shop, the last of three hemp stores. Other substantial stone buildings include the South Saw Mills (c1847) and Smithery (1857). There are two covered building slips. No.1 Slip (SX 452540), c1763 and relaid 1941, has a timber roof of c1814; the Scrieve Board of the 1830s is floored over and clad in corrugated iron. No.1 Dock, with a basin and dry dock, was reconstructed in 1834 on the site of the first dry dock of 1691-3 (SX 448544). An 1838 iron swing bridge crosses the Camber, a canal for stores (SX 447542). Ships were built until 1971 at the South Yard, the largest ever being the battleships *Warspite* and *Royal Oak* in 1913-14. Northwards, the Morice Yard includes the Gun Wharf 1718-25, designed by Sir John Vanbrugh (SX 448549).

These yards are separated from the main North Yard by the Torpoint Ferry approach, but were linked by a tunnel in 1856. The Keyham Steam Yard opened in 1853, with dry docks, basins and the Keyham Factory, a complex of machine shops, foundries, storehouses and rigging houses. The dry docks became the covered Frigate Complex in 1975. Northwards, the Great Extension Works, built in 1896-1907 by contractor Sir John Jackson, covers over 100 acres of basins and dry docks (SX 445565). Modernisation has continued to meet the needs of the Royal Navy, such as at Weston Mill

P5: Interior of No 1 covered slip, South Yard, Devonport
*Photo: Plymouth Naval Base Museum*

P5: No 1 covered slip, South Yard, Devonport
*Photo: Plymouth Naval Base Museum*

Lake for servicing nuclear submarines in the 1980s. Devonport Management Ltd (DML) took over the dockyard in 1987, which was fully privatised ten years later. A visit to the **Plymouth Naval Base Museum** in the South Dockyard is recommended.

## P6 LEIGHAM TUNNEL
SX 514586 ✳

The granite north portal of the Plymouth & Dartmoor Railway's 620-yd (566 m) Leigham Tunnel of 1823 is tucked in beside Plym Bridge Lane. The tunnel was an air raid shelter in the World War II.

## P7 MILLBAY DOCKS
SX 468539 ■ ✳

Smeaton had a workyard in Mill Bay for his Eddystone lighthouse. In 1844, Millbay Pier was designed by James Rendel for Thomas Gill, who owned limestone quarries nearby. It was altered by Brunel in the 1850s and lengthened in 1903. The SS *Great Britain* berthed here in 1845 and the Great Western Dock Co appointed Brunel to design a harbour to compete with Sutton Harbour. Brunel's inner floating basin with lock gates was built in 1853-7 but storms delayed full opening until 1859. After a link was made in 1850 from the South Devon Railway, a mail and passenger service was established with transatlantic liners calling at Plymouth, a trade which continued until the 1960s. Today, ferry services to France and Spain operate from the western side, where a graving dock was infilled to make space for the terminus. Part of the harbour is a marina and the liner passenger terminus, warehouses and Pier Hotel have been demolished. A three-storey octagonal Customs house, designed by George Wightwick in 1850, survives at Millbay Pier (SX 471533).

## P8 OLD TOWN STREET CONDUIT
Tavistock Road
SX 482551 ✳

Moved and set into the side of Drake's Place Reservoir in 1874, this historic conduit house from the Plymouth Leat has a granite inscription reading: made in the maioraltie of John Trelawyne 1598.

## P9 PLYMOUTH BREAKWATER
The Sound
SX 470504 ✳

Designed by John Rennie, and finished after his death in 1821 by his son Sir John, this great breakwater one mile (1.6 km) long protects the anchorage of Plymouth Sound and is clearly seen from the Hoe. It was constructed in 1812-41 on four

P7: The octagonal Custom House, Millbay Pier

P12: Royal Albert Bridge

shoals, when over 3 million tons of Oreston limestone were deposited from special vessels. The top surface was completed with dressed limestone and Cornish and Dartmoor granite in the 1850s and 60s. The west end has a granite lighthouse, built in 1844 to the design of Walker and Burgess; the east end has a beacon. In 1861-8, a formidable Victorian fort was added just inside the breakwater.

## P10 PLYM VALLEY RAILWAY

Marsh Mills

SX 520571                                                ❑ *

Part of the South Devon & Tavistock Railway (1859-1962) has been relaid for working restored steam locomotives. Northwards, the Plym Valley Cycleway follows the course which has four viaducts and a tunnel within a few miles.

## P11 RADFORD LAKE LIMEKILN

Hooe

SX 506527                                                      *

Mayer Way passes between this unusual limekiln and the Radford Lake folly and boathouse. Instead of arches, the drawholes are gained through two small doorways, one using part of a granite press

as a lintel. The pot is filled and the overgrown quarry is behind.

## P12 ROYAL ALBERT BRIDGE

St Budeaux

SX 435587                                                      *

Opened in 1859 just before his death, Brunel's great masterpiece afforded the first railway crossing into Cornwall, a function still served by its single track. Approached by a viaduct from each end, the two main spans are supported by a central pier of cast-iron columns on a stone base. Each 445-ft (135 m) span has arched wrought-iron tubes and suspension chains. They were built on shore, floated out and raised in 1857-8. Alongside, the suspension Tamar Bridge has carried road traffic since 1961, replacing the old Saltash chain ferry (first started in 1833 by Rendel), the landing slips of which remain.

## P13 ROYAL WILLIAM VICTUALLING YARD

Stonehouse

SX 461536                                                      *

Impressive architecture on a grand scale on the south side of Stonehouse Creek, built by John Rennie in 1826-35 at a cost of £1.5m. The granite entrance archway has carved ox heads, the whole surmounted by a statue of King William IV. Inside, the premises included a cooperage, stores, slaughterhouse, and bakehouse, powered by two 40HP engines to produce ships' biscuits. Quays at the frontage allowed for the transfer of stores to Naval vessels. Since becoming redundant, the yard has been subjected to redevelopment. It can be seen from the foot passenger Cremyll Ferry that departs from Admiral's Hard.

P8: Old Town Conduit of 1598, Plymouth

## P14 SMEATON'S TOWER

The Hoe
SX 477538 ❑

P14: Smeaton's Tower

The third Eddystone lighthouse of 1759, of important design by John Smeaton using dovetailed blocks of Cornish granite and Portland stone for the exterior and interior. Its foundation rock became undermined and it was replaced in 1882 by a taller granite tower designed by Sir James Douglass. The old lighthouse was dismantled and re-erected on the Hoe, from where its stump and the new lighthouse can be seen on a clear day 14 miles (22 km) SSW.

## P15 STONEHOUSE WATER TOWER

Stonehouse
SX 468548 ✳

An eighteenth-century octagonal stone tower, behind the high wall surrounding the Royal Naval Hospital grounds, on a high point at the top of Eldad Hill.

## P16 SUTTON HARBOUR

SX 484544 ✳

On the west side, Sutton Wharf was built in 1813-15 by the Sutton Pool Co. The Sutton Harbour & Dock Co built North Quay in 1849-50, but further ambitions were lost to Millbay Docks. Despite the conversion of old warehouses for apartments over-

P13: The Royal William Yard's impressive entrance

looking a yacht marina, Sutton Wharf and North Quay still retain their stone setts and railway tracks; the former has an iron crane of 1850 by John E. Mare of Plymouth. Around the Barbican side is the Customs House of 1820. The 1896 fish market with cast-iron work from Willoughby's foundry in Plymouth is now a tourist amenity, the fish-landing quay having moved across the harbour. Former offices of the London & South Western Railway are also here. The West Pier (1791-9) has the famous Mayflower Steps and monuments commemorating famous departures, such as the Pilgrim Fathers; another monument relates to water supply. Elsewhere in Sutton Harbour, Johnsons Quay was the terminus of the Plymouth & Dartmoor Railway, but is now unrecognisable.

## P17 TORPOINT FERRY

Devonport
SX 448551 ✳

Three large diesel-powered chain ferries cross here. The first steam chain ferry or floating bridge, started service in 1834 and proved most suitable for crossing the busy tidal Tamar estuary to Torpoint in Cornwall. It was designed by James Meadows Rendel, who was also responsible for the Saltash and Dartmouth ferries.

P17: Torpoint Ferry, c1900

**27**

From Devon's southernmost tip at Prawle Point to the granite upland of Dartmoor, 'the land of enclosed pastures' is dissected by rivers which supplied power to numerous small mills. On Dartmoor, extractive industries include granite working, tin streaming and mining, an opencast wolfram site and extensive china clay workings. Elsewhere, Devonian limestone was quarried for stone and limeburning around Yealmpton. Slate was quarried along a belt near Kingsbridge and in the Plym valley. Brickmaking still takes place at Steer Point, Brixton.

Numerous tollhouses are evidence of turnpike roads. Brunel's broad-gauge South Devon Railway was opened between Totnes and Plymouth in 1849, a hilly section including steep climbs, viaducts and a tunnel. There were later branches to Ashburton **(TE6)**, Kingsbridge and Yealmpton. Industrial railways served clay works at Lee Moor and Redlake. The sea was an important highway until the early twentieth century with barges sailing to small quays and limekilns along the deeply penetrating estuaries. Totnes, at the head of the navigable Dart, is the most important town, with other centres at Dartmouth, Ivybridge and Kingsbridge.

The Industrial Revolution owes rural South Hams a great debt. The pioneering steam engineer Thomas Savery was born near Modbury, while Thomas Newcomen came from Dartmouth, William Cookworthy, the discoverer of china clay, was born at Kingsbridge, and Charles Babbage, inventor of an early calculator, was a Totnes man.

## SH1 AVONWICK TOLLHOUSE
Avonwick
SX 716583                                          ✻
'Bridge Cottage' is a two-storey tollhouse in good order on the north side of Avonwick Bridge (River Avon), not to be confused with a lodge opposite.

## SH2 TUCKENHAY PAPER MILL
Cornworthy
SX 817558                                          ✻
An impressive building with a clock tower in an unexpected location in a quiet valley near a creek off the Dart. Built as a cloth mill, it became a paper mill c1830. It has now been converted to accommodation. The course of the mill's leat can be seen along the valleyside from a silted up mill pond at SX 815555. Tuckenhay corn mill is across the road.

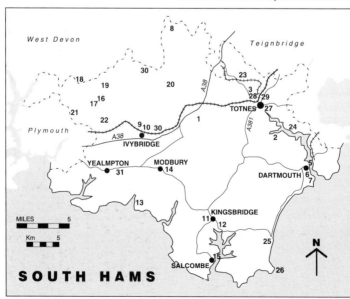

SOUTH HAMS

SH3: Lower Textile Mill, Dartington

SH3: Shinner's Bridge limekilns, Dartiington

## SH3 LOWER TEXTILE MILL AND LIMEKILNS

Dartington
SX 790621                               ✳
The Dartington estate's stone-built mill of 1930-1, no longer used for weaving, beside the A385 near Shinner's Bridge, with the water supply, launder and turning waterwheel (by Willcocks of Buckfastleigh) all visible. Just upstream, the Shinner's Bridge limekilns (SX 789622) are preserved in a picnic area near the Dartington Cider Press Centre.

## SH4 DART ESTUARY

Dartmouth to Totnes
SX 870510 to SX 807603                   ✳
Best explored from the water, the estuary can be navigated all the way to Totnes. Small stone quays along the river and side creeks once served local villages and private houses. The deep water of the lower estuary has been used for laying-up ocean-going ships during times of trade depression. Philip's ship and boatyard is at Higher Noss Point (SX 880531). The Britannia Royal Naval College (SX 875520), built in 1899-1905, dominates upper Dartmouth and is another reminder of Devon's naval heritage.

## SH5 DARTMOUTH FERRIES

Dartmouth
SX 879519 and SX 879511                  ✳
The Higher Ferry (SX 879519) is a crossing for the A379, where a diesel-powered paddle car ferry of 1960 is guided by two steel ropes. It began in 1831 with a steam chain ferry by James Rendel, designer of the Saltash and Torpoint ferries. The Lower Ferry (SX 879511) is somewhat quainter, powered by a motor boat alongside. A ferry crossed from the railway at Kingswear to a special GWR terminus on Dartmouth Quay, now the Station Restaurant (SX 879513).

## SH6 NEWCOMEN ENGINE

Dartmouth
SX 878514                               ❑
A preserved Newcomen atmospheric engine with a 22-in diameter cylinder was erected here in Thomas Newcomen's home town in 1963 to commemorate the 300th anniversary of the inventor's birth. Dating from the 1720s, it is said to be the oldest engine in existence, having first worked at Griff Colliery, Midlands, and later at Hawksbury Junction on the Coventry Canal from 1821 to 1913.

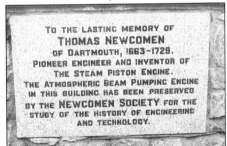

TO THE LASTING MEMORY OF
**THOMAS NEWCOMEN**
OF DARTMOUTH, 1663-1729.
PIONEER ENGINEER AND INVENTOR OF
THE STEAM PISTON ENGINE.
THE ATMOSPHERIC BEAM PUMPING ENGINE
IN THIS BUILDING HAS BEEN PRESERVED
BY THE NEWCOMEN SOCIETY FOR THE
STUDY OF THE HISTORY OF ENGINEERING
AND TECHNOLOGY.

SH6: The Newcomen memorial

An electric motor gives motion to this memorial engine in a building adjoining the Tourist Information Centre in Royal Avenue Gardens.

## SH7 WARFLEET BREWERY

Dartmouth
SX 881503                               ✳
A large stone building, originally Arthur H Holdsworth's paper mill of 1819 and powered by a large waterwheel. It closed in 1832 and later became a brewery. John Madocks & Co. brewed 'Barley wine from the English Rhine' in 1875-85, followed by the Bartlett family's Wafleet Pale Ales until 1927. Brewing ceased in 1929. It is now the Dartmouth Pottery, having become a pottery in 1948. In the early nineteenth century, there were three watermills, a ropewalk and two limekilns here **29** at Warfleet, a small creek off the lower Dart harbour.

SH10 Stowford Paper Mill, Ivybridge

## SH8 WHEAL EMMA LEAT
Holne
SX 668718 ✳

The course of a 9-mile (14.4 km) leat from Foxtor Mires (West Devon) contours Holne Moor to feed the River Mardle, supplying water for the Wheal Emma and Brookwood copper mine (SX 717675), which has the remains of wheelpits and two engine houses. The leat, with others, is crossed four times by a lane between Combestone Tor and Venford Reservoir.

## SH9 IVYBRIDGE VIADUCT
Ivybridge
SX 636569 ✳

A curving stone-arched viaduct above Ivybridge, built in 1893 when the line was doubled a year after conversion from broad to standard gauge. The stone piers of Brunel's original viaduct of 11 timber spans are alongside. Other viaducts around the southern flanks of Dartmoor include Glazebrook (SX 688591), Bittaford (SX 666570), Blachford (SX 608583) and Slade (SX 600581) .

## SH10 STOWFORD PAPER MILL
Ivybridge
SX 636566 ■

An impressive mill block overlooks the town, with three brick storeys above a granite base. A paper mill of 1787 was bought in 1849 by John Allen and enlarged in 1862. Originally water-powered, a steam engine was installed in 1914. Portals Ltd took over in 1923, and Wiggins Teape seven years later.

SH12: New Bridge across Bowcombe Creek, Kingsbridge

SH10: Gilkes turbine from Glanville's Mill, Ivybridge

Today, Arjo Wiggins produce high quality watermarked papers. Displayed in a car park just below is a 1937 Gilkes water turbine from Glanville's Mill, now a shopping centre in Ivybridge.

## SH11 KINGSBRIDGE
Kingsbridge
SX 734446 ✳
❏

Kingsbridge was a port at the head of the Kingsbridge estuary, where there were mills and a foundry.

William Cookworthy (1705-80), the discoverer of china clay and inventor of English porcelain, was born here although his chemist business was in Plymouth. The **Cookworthy Museum** in Fore Street has displays on local history industry and transport (closed for renovation during 1998).

## SH12 NEW BRIDGE
Kingsbridge
SX 745432 ✳

Also known as Charleton Bridge, a five-arched stone bridge, built 1828-31 to take the Kingsbridge-Dartmouth turnpike across the mouth of Bowcombe Creek. The east arch was built in c1900 to replace an opening section which allowed vessels to pass upstream to serve a corn mill, limekilns and slate quarries. James Rendel designed a hydraulic-powered drawbridge in 1831, but this was replaced by a swing bridge in 1845.

## SH13 WONWELL SLIP
Kingston
SX 620477 ✳

This served the Kingston area until 1917, importing coal and limestone for the now ruined limekilns beside the sandy beach of the Erme estuary.

## SH14 MODBURY
Modbury
SX 657516 ✳

Modbury was a local centre for manufacturing woollens in the seventeenth and eighteenth centuries. It has three water conduits, one in Brownston

Street, where the Literary & Scientific Institution (now a dwelling) was established in 1840. Thomas Savery, the inventor of an engine to 'for raise Water by the force of fire' was reputedly born nearby at Shilston. He was a partner with Thomas Newcomen of Dartmouth for a while after 1705. A tollhouse stands at a junction on the A379 at SX 664510.

## SH15 SALCOMBE
Salcombe
SX 741391                              ✳ ❑
Near the mouth of the Kingsbridge estuary, Salcombe was home to a fleet of fast sailing schooners engaged on the citrus fruit trade with Spain and the Azores and the Newfoundland fish trade in the nineteenth century. There is a **maritime museum** (SX 741391) and the lifeboat house at South Sands, 1878-1925, is of architectural interest.

## SH16 LEE MOOR CHINA CLAY WORKS
Shaugh Prior
SX 570625 and SX 565610                    ■
China clay has been exploited at Lee Moor since 1830. A large brick and tile works operated at Torycombe from the 1850s until 1943. Today there are huge clay pits and modern processing works which have destroyed much evidence of the early days. There are other large workings nearby at Cholwichtown, Headon and Shaugh Lake.

## SH17 LEE MOOR TRAMWAY
Shaugh Prior
SX 569615                              ✳
A 7-mile (11.2 km) tramway of 2 ft 6 in gauge was opened in 1858 to bring clay down from Lee Moor to Plymouth harbour. It was horse worked, although steam locomotives were used between its two inclines after 1899. At the top end, part of the Torycombe incline remains (SX 569615), with a lookout hut known as the 'bell house'. The foot of the Cann Wood incline is near Plym Bridge (SX 524586). Most of the tramway closed in 1947 when a pipeline was laid to carry clay to dries at Marsh Mills, but the horse-worked lower part remained until 1960. Locomotive *Lee Moor No.2* is preserved at the National Trust's Saltram House (SX 521555).

## SH18 SHAUGH BRIDGE CHINA CLAY WORKS
Shaugh Prior
SX 534636                              ✳
Nineteenth-century clay processing works, to which clay was piped down from pits at Shaugh Lake and Wigford Down near Cadover Bridge. Behind the Dewerstone car park can be seen the long

SH21: Cann Quarry Canal and Tramway

buttressed linhay (store) and drying kiln, with settling tanks in the woods above.

## SH19 TROWLESWORTHY TOR QUARRIES
Shaugh Prior
SX577646                               ✳
A reddish granite was worked here until the 1880s at a small quarry, with tips and crane base close to Little Trowlesworthy Tor, and abandoned blocks and a 'drum' of granite 5ft 6ins (1.7 m) diameter on the open moor.

## SH20 SHIPLEY BRIDGE WORKS
South Brent
SX 680629                              ✳
In 1846-50, a naphtha works at Shipley Bridge was supplied with peat brought down from the moors on the 3-mile (4.8 km) Zeal Tor Tramway with wooden rails on granite sleeper blocks. This was soon abandoned and in 1858 the Brent Moor Clay Co. converted the works to clay dries and used the tramway to serve its pits. Overgrown clay settling tanks can be seen above the ruins by the car park at Shipley Bridge.

## SH21 CANN QUARRY
Sparkwell
SX 524596                              NT ✳
Here in the wooded Plym valley is flooded slate quarry and at least three large pits for waterwheels which drove saws and planing machines. A short canal was built in 1829 by the Earl of Morley from Cann Quarry to a tramway at Marsh Mills, but within six years the canal was extended alongside the canal; its stone sleeper blocks survive. Quarrying **31** ceased in the 1860s. There is also the Cann Via-

SH26: Start Point Lighthouse

## SH24 STOKE GABRIEL TIDEMILL DAM
Stoke Gabriel
SX 848569       *
A large mill pool is held back by the dam causeway of Stoke Gabriel tidemill, which appears as two mill buildings and two waterwheels in a painting of 1793 by Willam Payne. The mill is recorded in 1850.

## SH25 BEESANDS QUARRY
Stokenham
SX 822416       **NT** *
An example of several slate quarries in the area, this one in the cliffs near Torcross and accessible at low tide. It was known as Start Bay Slate Quarry in 1855 when offered for sale with a steam engine, slate planing machine and pump.

## SH26 START POINT LIGHTHOUSE
Stokenham
SX 829371       *
A landmark on a craggy promontory jutting into the English Channel. The lighthouse was built in 1836 to the design of James Walker with a straight stone-built tower and a crenellated top. Now fully automated. Some keepers' accommodation, built 1871, survived recent cliff-falls; their old garden plots are just below on the north side.

## SH27 TOTNES QUAYS
Totnes
SX 806601       *
Warehouses and a malting at New Walk alongside a quay on the tidal Dart have been converted to housing. At St Peters Quay, the Steam Packet Inn adjoins a John Symonds & Co's former cider factory and warehouse (converted to housing); nearby are two limekilns. Lower down, Baltic Wharf was developed in the 1960s for the timber trade, where Francis Reeves had begun imports early in the century. Steamer Quay is across the water. Upstream, an elegant stone bridge of 1826-28 by Charles Fowler spans the Dart (SX 807603); at the town end is a two-storeyed tollhouse.

## SH28 BRUNEL ATMOSPHERIC PUMPING STATION
Totnes
SX 802609       *
Next to the railway station and now part of the Unigate creamery. Others survivors are at Starcross (TE26) and Torre (TO12).

## SH29 TOWN MILL
Totnes
SX 806604       ❏
Refurbished as a Tourist Information Centre, the mill has some restored machinery on the ground floor and a low breast wheel (Willcocks of

duct (1907) of the old Tavistock branch railway. Access is from a car park at Plym Bridge (SX 524586).

## SH22 HEMERDON MINE
Sparkwell
SX 572586       *
A large wolfram and tin stockwork was prospected and worked opencast in 1917-19, and in 1943-44. A footpath passes the old excavation and the great mill of the early 1940s, now a partly-roofed concrete skeleton stripped of its machinery. A scheme to make Hemerdon the largest wolfram opencast mine in Europe was abandoned when tungsten prices fell in the 1980s. Across the valley to the west is the chimney stack of Bottle Hill Mine (SX 565588).

## SH23 STAVERTON BRIDGE
Staverton
SX 784637       *
A medieval stone bridge of c1413 with seven arches across the River Dart, near the preserved South Devon Railway's station and Bridge Mill, a former turbine-powered roller mill.

Buckfastleigh) brought from Bellamarsh Mill, Chudleigh.

## SH30 REDLAKE CHINA CLAY WORKS AND TRAMWAY

Ugborough

SX 659566 to SX 646669 ✳

Redlake (SX 646669), a remote spot at an altitude of 1,475 ft (450 m), has flooded china clay pits, waste tips and the remains of workshops and workers' hostel. Clay was separated in sand and mica drags at Greenhill (SX 650657) and piped in a slurry down to the dries at Cantrel (SX 659566). The Cantrel dries are now an agricultural engineering works. A 3-ft gauge tramway, 7¹/₂ miles (12 km) long, serviced the clay pits from 1910 until 1933. An incline ascended from Cantrel and thereafter the course of the line is still traced across the moors to Redlake.

## SH31 YEALMBRIDGE TOLLHOUSE AND TOLL HUT

Yealmpton

SX 590520 ✳

Tollhouse of the Modbury Trust beside the bridge, two-storeyed with Gothic windows and doorways, with a stone toll hut just to the east (SX 593520) to catch travellers joining from a side road.

SH31:Yealmbridge stone toll house

Teignbridge is a hilly district, bounded by Dartmoor, Haldon Hill and the coast. Woollen textiles were once important around Ashburton and Buckfastleigh, where there are still traces of mills and drying lofts. Ashburton was a stannary town for the tin workings on Dartmoor. To the east, the Teign valley had silver-lead, micaceous hematite and barytes mines, as well as roadstone quarries in basalt at Bridford and Trusham. In the Bovey Basin, high grade ball clay is still worked in open pits and underground; lignite was once mined here too. Pottery and brickmaking industries also developed in this area. Granite quarrying is dominated by the famous Haytor quarries and their tramways. Limestone was quarried at Chudleigh and Buckfastleigh (where it was polished as a 'marble') and is still quarried at Stonecombe for roadstone; disused limekilns are common. There are some well engineered turnpike roads through this hilly country. The district has the spectacular coastal section of Brunel's railway between Dawlish and Teignmouth. Branches included lines to Ashburton, Moretonhampstead and the Teign valley. Newton Abbot grew after the railway came in 1846. There was an important locomotive and carriage works here, but other industries have been woollen textiles, tanning, cider making and malting. Clay barges once plied the Teign estuary and the short Stover and Hackney Canals. Teignmouth is still a busy exporter of clay.

## TE1 BELFORD MILL
Ashburton
SX 754716                                       ✳

Also known as the Coffin Mill because of its narrow shape in a constricted site. Having been a woollen mill it was converted to corn milling in the mid nineteenth century, but this warehouse part with a weather-boarded drying loft is now a house.

## TE2 DRUID MINE
Ashburton
SX 745716                                       ✳

An engine house and brick topped stack in a wood close to a lane. The mine worked unsuccessfully for copper on and off from the 1850s to 70s. The engine house, enlarged in 1869 to take a 56-in engine, has iron tie plates by the Tavistock Foundry.

*above:* TE3: Pottery kilns at Bovey Tracey
*right above:* TE4: Machine room and Californian stamps at Kelly Mine                    *Photo: Kelly Mine*
*right below:* TE4: Restored launder and waterwheel at Kelly Mine                    *Photo: Stephen Lygo*

## TE3 BOVEY POTTERY WORKS

Bovey Tracey
SX 815772 ❑

Bovey Tracey potteries were founded c1750, and the Indeo and Folly Potteries were important rivals until closure in 1836. The latter reopened in 1843, was enlarged and continued until 1957. There are three preserved bottle-shaped muffle kilns of 1896-1900 and a small **museum** run by Teign Valley Glass and the House of Marbles. Lignite was mined locally for fuel. Nearby, the modernised Candy Tiles works (SX 834760) produces glazed tiles.

## TE4 KELLY MINE

Bovey Tracey
SX 795818 ☆

Micaceous hematite or shiney ore was once used for drying ink as 'Devon Sand', but was later in demand for anti-corrosive paints. Of several small mines in the area, Kelly Mine had worked in the 1790s, was reopened in 1879-91 and then in 1900-46 by Ferrebron Manufacturing Co. The Kelly Mine Preservation Society has been active here restoring drying and dressing sheds, a turbine, waterwheel, leat, Californian stamps and inclined tramway. Great Rock Mine (SX 827816), the last of these mines, closed in 1969. Access is by arrangement with the preservation group, c/o 10 Cardinal Avenue, St Budeaux, Plymouth PL5 1UW.

## TE5 RIVERSIDE MILL

Bovey Tracey
SX 815782 ❑

The building was a coach house, for Riverside or Bridge House, built in 1854 with a waterwheel

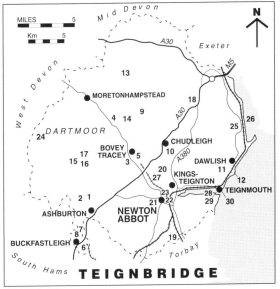

**TEIGNBRIDGE**

alongside to pump water up to a tank in the tower. The water supplied the house, gardens and stable yard. 'Riverside Mill' is now a gallery and cafe of the Devon Guild of Craftsmen.

## TE6 BUCKFASTLEIGH STATION

Buckfastleigh
SX 746663 ❑

Here are sidings with rolling stock and a museum containing *Tiny*, a broad-gauge locomotive with a vertical boiler, built by Sara & Co of Plymouth in 1868 to work at Sutton Harbour. The Buckfastleigh, Totnes & South Devon Railway (1872-1962) was broad gauge for its first 20 years. It became the steam Dart Valley Railway in 1969, now the South

TE7: New wheel at Higher Buckfast Mill, Buckfastleigh

TE8: Hamlyns Mill, Buckfastleigh

Devon Railway, running for 7 miles (1.2 km) along the Dart valley via Staverton to Totnes, both in South Hams. The upper part of the line disappeared when the A30 was dualled, but Ashburton's covered station shed survives as a garage at SX 757698.

## TE7 HIGHER BUCKFAST MILL
Buckfastleigh
SX 739674                                             ✳
This restored early nineteenth-century woollen mill has a long wooden launder alongside supplying water to a new wheel. The adjacent wing is now the Buckfast monastic produce shop. Lower Buckfast Mill is a modern textile operation.

## TE8 HAMLYNS MILL
Buckfastleigh
SX 739662                                             ✳
An impressive four-storey woollen mill of Hamlyn Bros, in grey limestone with brick details, and restored as Hamlyn House for offices and light industrial use. The adjacent Mardle House has received similar attention. Just west is the Devonia Skins tannery.

## TE9 WHEAL EXMOUTH
Christow
SX 838830                                             ✳
A large pumping engine house at Porter's Shaft has been converted to a house. Its 70-inch beam engine, built by J E Mare & Co of Plymouth, worked here in 1854-62 and survives at Prestongrange Colliery near Edinburgh. There is an octagonal chim-

ney stack and a second stack with an ornate top. All this was because the mine was close to Lord Exmouth's house. Recorded output in 1851-74 was 10,897 tons of lead ore, 132,789 oz of silver and a small quantity of zinc ore. Half a mile (0.8 km) south the richer Frank Mills Mine and its waste tips are more ruinous (SX 837820).

## TE10 TOWN MILL
Chudleigh
SX 869795                                             ❑
Part of the Wheel Craft Workshops, Clifford Street, a 20 ft x 3 ft 6 in (6.1 m x 1.1 m) iron backshot wheel made by Ivor Hall of Ideford in 1860, is often seen turning. The mill worked until c1940 and most of the machinery inside is complete and can be viewed when the craft studios and tea-rooms are open.

## TE11 STRAND MILLS WATERWHEEL
Dawlish
SX 962767                                             ✳
Easily missed in Brunswick Place, a large iron backshot waterwheel 30 ft (9.1m) diameter by A Bodley of Exeter is tucked away alongside the former Strand or Torbay Mills, now the Old Mill tea-rooms.

## TE12 SOUTH DEVON RAILWAY SEA WALL
Dawlish to Teignmouth
SX 978779 to SX 945732                                ✳
Sea wall built in 1846 for Brunel's short-lived atmospheric railway, altered and repaired after land-

TE9: Engine house at Wheal Exmouth, Christow

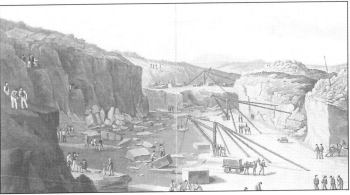

slips and sea erosion. A memorable journey for rail passengers, as the line passes through five tunnels in the red sandstone cliffs between Dawlish station (SX 964767) and Teignmouth. For walkers, a promenade follows the wall each side of the tunnel section.

### TE13 STEPS BRIDGE IRON MILLS
Dunsford
SX 807884 ■
A Morris & Sons work tilt hammers and drop hammers to produce edge tools such as billhooks and sickles. There is a lowbreast waterwheel of 1821 which worked two tilt hammers until 1937.

### TE14 TOTTIFORD RESERVOIRS
Hennock and Christow
SX 810827 ✳
Three earth dams built for Torquay's water supply. The first was for Tottiford Reservoir in 1861-67 (SX 810827). This was soon found to be inadequate, so Kennick Reservoir (SX 806838) followed in 1881-84, and Trenchford Reservoir (SX 806823) in 1903-7. A filtration works was built below this last dam in 1912.

### TE15 HAYTOR QUARRIES
Ilsington
SX 759774 ✳
Granite quarries were begun in 1820 by George Templer for the London Bridge contract. The main Haytor quarry is depicted in a print of 1825 with quarrymen hard at work, but activity had stopped by 1860. A broken timber crane and winch lie on the partly flooded floor. Holwell Quarry (SX 752778) has a curious stone shelter and there are seven small quarries on the moor. The coarse granite was used in London Bridge, National Gallery, Royal Exchange, Covent Garden Market, Fishmongers Hall and Buckingham Palace.

### TE16 HAYTOR VALE
Ilsington
SX 771772 ✳
A hostel (now the Rock Inn) and adjacent cottages were built c1820 by George Templer for his Haytor quarry workers, a necessary act to maintain a workforce high up on the edge of Dartmoor.

### TE17 HAYTOR GRANITE TRAMWAY
Ilsington and Bovey Tracey
SX 752778 to SX 848747 ✳
Built in 1820 by George Templer to carry granite 7 miles (11.2 km) down to the Stover Canal, for barging to Teignmouth and shipment to London. Wagons made the 1,200-ft (366 m) descent by gravity and were drawn back by horses. The tramway had granite 'plateway' sections up to 8 ft (2.4 m) long, with a gauge of 4 ft 3 in (1.3 m). Much can be traced across the moor, with points and 2 miles (3.25 km) of branches to quarries at Haytor, Holwell Tor and beyond. Some track also remains in Yarner Wood. The lower part was built over by the Moretonhampstead railway in 1861-2.

### TE18 HALDON TOLLHOUSE
Kenn
SX 908842 ✳
Now by-passed by the A38 on the steep northeast slope of Great Haldon Hill, a solid tollhouse with stone Gothic windows, built by the Plymouth and Exeter Road Trust in 1842.

### TE19 LONG BURROW WINDMILL
Kingskerswell
SX 872658 ✳
A tapered sandstone tower on a hill at 453 ft (138 m), beside a lane just south of North Whilborough.

### TE20 BALL CLAY WORKS
Kingsteignton
SX 860750 ■ **37**
An extensive area of the Bovey Basin ball clay, ac-

TE23: Tuckers Maltings, Newton Abbot

tively worked by ECC Ball Clays and Watts, Blake, Bearne & Co, is best seen from the B3193 between Kingsteignton and Chudleigh Knighton. These working pits and industrial areas are not open to the public and are dangerous.

## TE21 BRADLEY MILLS
Bradley Lane, Newton Abbot
SX 853711                                           ■
John Vicary & Sons had a wool processing mill here from the mid-nineteenth century until 1972. It was rebuilt after fires in 1883 and 1921. The firm also had a large tannery until the 1940s. Now converted to other industrial use.

## TE22 NEWTON ABBOT RAILWAY STATION
Newton Abbot
SX 867712                                      ✳ ❏
The tall station building of 1926 hints of this former important junction where some buildings remain of a large locomotive and carriage works. A signal gantry is preserved at the junction of Torquay and Brunel Roads (SX 868709). **Newton Abbot Town and Great Western Railway Museum** is in St Paul's Road (SX 864713).

## TE23 TUCKERS MALTINGS
Teign Road, Newton Abbot
SX 868715                                           ❏
An impressive range of stone-built maltings and warehouses of 1900 along the full length of Teign Road. Edwin Tucker & Sons (established 1831) operate the only traditional working malthouse open to the public in England. There are guided tours and the small Teignworthy Brewery is attached.

## TE24 BIRCH TOR AND VITIFER MINE
North Bovey
SX 682810                                            ✳
Just east of the Warren House Inn. Though there were probably medieval workings in the valley, this major site worked intermittently from the mid-eighteenth century until 1883 and then 1903-26, the last tin mine on Dartmoor. There are extensive areas of surface and underground workings, with remains of mine buildings, the mine captain's house, miners' house, carpenter's shop, wheel pits, etc. A leat brought water from the East Dart over 7 miles (11.2 km) away. An impressive run of deep openworks across Headland Warren (SX 689809) was part of East Birch Tor Mine.

## TE25 COCKWOOD LIMEKILNS
Starcross
SX 974808                                            ✳
Double limekilns of curious design stand in a garden beside the A379 just south of Starcross. Limestone and fuel were brought here by sea, for Cockwood was a trading creek on the Exe estuary until Brunel's railway blocked off the entrance to all but the smallest craft in 1846.

## TE26 STARCROSS ATMOSPHERIC PUMPHOUSE
Starcross
SX 977818                                            ✳
Brunel's pumphouse, in coarse red sandstone with pale limestone arches, used in 1847-8 for the experimental atmospheric section of the South Devon Railway between Exeter and Newton Abbot. Three Cornish boilers powered two Boulton & Watt engines for exhausting the air from the pipes laid between the rails. The chimney was once much higher. Now converted internally as the headquarters of the Starcross Angling and Cruising Club.

## TE27 STOVER CANAL
Teigngrace
SX 848747                                            ✳
Built in 1792 by James Templer of Stover House to carry ball clay at first and later, Haytor granite. Barges rigged like Viking ships sailed down the

TE25: Cockwood limekilns, Starcross

Teign estuary to Teignmouth. Later, strings of barges were towed by motor boats until the canal fell out of use and was closed in 1943. Visible survivals along the 2-mile (3.2 km) canal include the basin wharf and a crane base at Ventiford (SX 848747), the top lock at Teigngrace (SX 850741), where barges were built, and a bridge dated 1798 and clay cellars at Teign Bridge (SX 856733).

## TE28 SHALDON BRIDGE
Teignmouth
SX 931729                                              *
A timber bridge 1,671 ft (509 m) long across the lower Teign estuary between Teignmouth and Shaldon was built in 1825-27 by Roger Hopkins (engineer of the Plymouth & Dartmoor Railway). It had 34 spans, with the northern one swinging, and was said to be the longest wooden bridge in England. It was reconstructed with 24 spans in 1931-2, with the original limestone and granite causeways still carrying the road at each end. At the

TE26: Atmospheric pumping station, Starcross

Teignmouth end, a fine tollhouse on the corner functioned until 1948.

## TE29 NEW QUAY
Teignmouth
SX 939727                                              *
Built of large granite blocks in 1825-7 for shipping Haytor granite to London. Quarried granite was barged down the estuary from the Stover Canal and stored on the quay. The present quays for handling ball clay and other commodities can be seen from here just upstream.

## TE30 TEIGNMOUTH LIGHTHOUSE
Teignmouth
SX 940725                                              *
A small grey limestone lighthouse, built in 1845 to guide ships past the sand spit at the mouth of the Teign. It once stood alone but is now incorporated into the Promenade and a car park. Teignmouth's iron pier of 1865 has seen better days.

TE30: Teignmouth lighthouse

TE28: Shaldon Bridge and tollhouse

**39**

A mostly urban district around Torbay, once an anchorage for the Channel Fleet during the Napoleonic Wars. This is the mild Devon Riviera where Torquay and Paignton are the main resorts. Brixham, famous for its fishing fleet, has a large breakwater. There were extensive cliff quarries in limestone at Berry Head, as well as Petit Tor (marble) and Long Quarry Point at Torquay. Iron ore was worked at Sharkham Point. Torbay has an unusually high number of surviving windmill towers. Industries included a terracotta works and a marble works at St Marychurch, Torquay, while Paignton was known for its trade in cider. Brunel's ill-fated atmospheric railway was intended to reach Torquay and a pumping engine house survives at Torre. There were branches to Kingswear and Brixham. Babbacombe has a cliff railway. Isaac Merritt Singer, founder of the sewing machine company, built Oldway Mansion at Paignton in 1875. It was much altered by his third son Paris in 1904-7 in the style of the Palace of Versailles.

## TO1 BERRY HEAD LIGHTHOUSE
Brixham
SX 946566                                                    ✳
A tiny lighthouse of 1906, only 15 ft (4.5 m) high yet one of the highest in Britain because it is 190 ft (58 m) above sea level. It was once worked by a weight in a shaft 150 ft (46 m) deep. The limestone cliffs on the north side were quarried extensively for over 150 years until 1969 when a country park was created. Berry Head is also noted for Napoleonic fortifications of 1803-5.

## TO2 BRIXHAM BREAKWATER
Brixham
SX 928570                                                    ✳
In the lee of Berry Head, from which limestone blocks were quarried, the 3,000-ft (914 m) breakwater was designed by James Rendel and built in 1843, with extensions in 1909 and 1912. The work gave protection to the fishing port of Brixham, which in the 1860s boasted 200 sailing trawlers of 40-50 tons. The Admiralty had an establishment for watering the navy.

## TO3 BRIXHAM TOLLHOUSE
Brixham
SX 915555                                                    ✳
Painted slate-hung tollhouse of two storeys prominent at the entry to Brixham, at the junction of New Road and Monksbridge Road. Built in 1790 for the Torquay Trust.

## TO4 GALMPTON WARBOROUGH WINDMILL
Galmpton
SX 889567                                                    ✳
A four-storeyed limestone tower about 35 ft (10.6 m) high is a landmark near the A379. The windmill may date from 1810 and worked until the 1880s.

## TO5 FERNACOMBE WINDMILL
Paignton
SX 875624                                                    ✳
A tapering sandstone tower 30 ft (9.1 m) high on Windmill Hill at Fernacombe, is the remains of a windmill believed to date from the late eighteenth century, but disused by the 1860s.

## TO6 PAIGNTON HARBOUR
Paignton
SX 896603                                                    ✳
The two-armed stone harbour was built in 1839 for local trade and now shelters fishing and passenger craft.

TO1: Berry Head's tiny lighthouse, near Brixham

TO4: Galmpton Warborough windmill tower

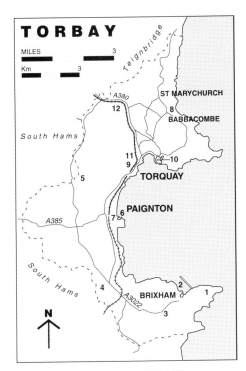

# TORBAY

MILES 3
Km 3

*Teignbridge*

A380
ST MARYCHURCH
12
8
BABBACOMBE
South Hams
11
9
10
5
TORQUAY
6
PAIGNTON
A385
7
4
BRIXHAM
3022
2
1
3
South Hams

N

## TO7 PAIGNTON-KINGSWEAR RAILWAY
Paignton
SX 890605 to SX 882511 ❑
Preserved steam railway run since 1972 in the tradition of the Great Western Railway from Paignton to Kingswear, via Churston. Works along the scenic 7-mile (11.2 km) line include the Greenway Tunnel. The original railway of 1864 had a branch (since closed) to Brixham. The GWR ran a passenger ferry across the estuary to Dartmouth.

## TO8 BABBACOMBE CLIFF RAILWAY
Torquay
SX 925658 ❑
The Babbacombe cliff railway was built in 1926. It drops 250 ft (76 m) down a wooded cliff to Oddicombe Beach.

## TO9 MANOR HOUSE HOTEL
Seaway Lane, Torquay
SX 903634 ☆
Formerly Chelston Cross, this house of architectural interest was the home of William Froude (1810-79), ship model research pioneer. In 1872 he built the world's first experimental tank for the Admiralty. It survives as a swimming pool.

TO8: Babbacombe cliff railway, Torquay

## TO10 TORQUAY HARBOUR
Torquay
SX 918633 ✳
The Haldon family built the inner harbour in 1806, followed by Haldon Pier in 1870. Later, the Princess Pier enclosed the outer harbour. This commercial harbour, which had an emigrant trade to Canada in the mid-nineteenth century, is now mostly for pleasure craft. William Shaw had a small shipbuilding yard under Beacon Hill in 1840-58.

## TO11 TORQUAY RAILWAY STATION
Rathmore Road, Torquay
SX 906635 ✳
Attractive single-storey station buildings of 1878 in grey limestone with towers mounted with slate roofs and iron cresting, a design similar to Teignmouth station. Cast-iron columns support the platform canopies and footbridge. Torre Station (SX 904648) is earlier and also of interest.

## TO12 TORRE PUMPING STATION
Newton Road, Torquay
SX 899662 ✳
Brunel's atmospheric railway pumping engine house, never used, with a tall limestone chimney with red sandstone top. It became Longpark Pottery, c1883-1972, and is now the premises of Frank H Mann Ltd, fruit and vegetable wholesalers.

TO12: Atmospheric pumping station, Torre

**41**

The Torridge District includes the valley of this river, the scenic and rocky Atlantic coast and a large expanse of culm measures in the west which provided poor agricultural land. It also includes Lundy Island, 12 miles (19 km) NNW of Hartland Point. Bideford is the largest town and, with Appledore/Northam, has been historically important for its overseas trade, shipbuilding and, latterly, as a resort area. Torrington and Holsworthy are historic market towns, the former having some industrial history. Otherwise, the district is sparsely populated, especially in the west towards the Cornish border. Apart from the buildings of a few factories in Bideford and Torrington, the industrial archaeology relates mainly to rural mills, limekilns and transport infrastructure. The latter includes the remains of two interesting rural canals, relics of minor railways and tollhouses of former turnpike roads, in addition to the historic harbour of Clovelly and the quays at Appledore and Bideford.

## TR1 COOPER & CO'S COLLAR FACTORY
Rope Walk, Bideford
SS 454269                                          *

A tall, narrow building of ten bays either side of a central loading bay in pale cream brick with red brick dressings. Built in the 1890s the central bay has a pediment and cupola. Cooper & Co had opened the town's second collar factory in 1886 in New Street and purchased the old rope walk as a site for this factory. Since closure, the factory has been used as a furniture depository and the name Blackmore's Depository survives.

## TR2 LONG BRIDGE
Bideford
SS 456264                                          *

A 24-arch masonry bridge over the River Torridge, 677 ft (206 m) long and dating from the thirteenth century when it was built of timber. It was widened in 1792-1810, 1865 and 1925 and major repairs made in 1968. The new high level bridge, visible downstream, has relieved this historic bridge of much through traffic.

## TR3 THE QUAY
Bideford
SS 455266                                          *

Bideford's attractive river quay is a reminder of its important maritime past. Its origins are obscure but a new quay was built by the Crown in 1663 and has been widened and extended since, last in 1889-90. The 'Old Customs House' (Bridgeland Street) and the street name 'Ropewalk' recall former maritime activity. In addition to overseas and coastal trade, ships were built in the town, formerly at Brunswick Wharf at East-the-Water until the late 1880s.

## TR4 VINCENT AND DUNCAN'S COLLAR FACTORY
Northam Road, Bideford
SS 449269                                          *

Opened in 1871, one of three factories used for collar making in Bideford. The site comprises the late Victorian factory, in Marland

TORRIDGE

TR2: Long Bridge, Bideford

brick with red dressings, formerly powered by a gas engine, and the three-storey Westcombe flour mill, built as a steam mill in 1827 and worked as such until c.1850. Extensions of 1881 can be seen on Northdown Road. High-starched collars were sewn on powered machines and finished here. The factory closed c1925 and is now in use by coal merchants and as a council depot.

## TR5 RAILWAY YARD
Kingsley Road, Bideford
SS 453270                                        ✳

The carriage shed (now a coach depot) and engine shed (a dairy depot) of the independent Bideford, Westward Ho! & Appledore Railway (1901-17) survive beside the road next to the football ground. At Appledore, there is a plaque on the rear wall of the terminus buildings (SS 464304).

## TR6 ORLEIGH MILL
Buckland Brewer
SS 437224                                        ■

A four-storey grist mill, rebuilt in 1884, with a cast-iron pitchback wheel 18 ft x 8 ft (5.5 m x 2.4 m) brought from the now-demolished Barnstaple town mills in 1939. The wheel has not worked for some

time but is capable of driving a pair of stones. A 1930s oil engine also survives. The leats are served by the rivers Yeo and Duntz. The mill is now part of a more recent animal feed manufactory.

## TR7 CLOVELLY HARBOUR
Clovelly
SS 318248                                        ✳

Historic small harbour protected by a curved pier, first erected in 1567 by the lord of the manor to provide a safe haven. A circular limekiln survives by the harbour. The difficulty of maintaining a harbour on this hostile coast is illustrated by the demise of Hartland Quay, destroyed by storms in 1896. There is a **maritime museum** at Hartland Quay (SS 223247).

## TR8 ROLLE CANAL BASIN AND TOWN MILLS
Great Torrington
SS 500184                                        ☆

From Taddiport Bridge a footpath (Rolle Road) follows the route of the former Torrington Canal below Castle Hill to the terminal basin and Town Mills. The mills, with surviving malthouse and crenellated house, were built c1825 alongside the canal basin which was entered via two tunnels, still visible immediately to the east of the river arches of the bridge. The mill, with a restored waterwheel, is part of the self-catering Orford Mill complex.

## TR9 TORRINGTON STATION
Great Torrington
SS 480198                                        ❏

Opened in 1872, when the railway was extended from Bideford, the station has a gabled two-storey house with single-storey waiting room and offices in stone. Nearby is the bridge over the Torridge. A wooden viaduct here carried the 3-ft (0.9 m) gauge Torrington & Marland Railway, built in 1880 and replaced by the standard-gauge North Devon & Cornwall Junction Light Railway to Halwill in 1925. The old railway line is now the Tarka Trail, a footpath/cycleway.

**43**

TR6: Orleigh Mill

TR10: Glove Factory, Great Torrington
*Photo: Marilyn Palmer*

## TR10 VAUGHAN'S GLOVE FACTORY
White's Lane, Great Torrington
SS 493192                          ✳
Described by Pevsner as the oddest building in the town, this factory resembles a chapel. It is of two storeys with attic windows in pale Marland brick with red brick Gothic arches. Carvings on the front show a glove press and glove. It was built in 1884 for manufacturing fabric fashion gloves. It is still in use by Vaughan, Tapscott Ltd.

## TR11 BUDE CANAL: STANBURY WHARF AND BLAGDONMOOR WHARF
Holsworthy Hamlets
SS 349051 and SS 362058            ✳
At 35¹/2 miles (57 km), James Green's Bude Canal (1825-1891) was the longest tub-boat canal in England and was built mainly to carry lime-rich sea sand to dress the poor soils of north-east Cornwall and north-west Devon. Most of the canal is in Corn-

TR14: Hallsannery limekiln
*Photo: Marilyn Palmer*

wall, but the Devon sections include a Holsworthy branch. The wharfinger's house and store/transit shed survive as farm buildings on the A388 at Stanbury Wharf Farm (SS 349051). The head of navigation was Blagdonmoor Wharf, which has another shed (SS 362058). Beyond this an overgrown cutting was for an extension towards Thornbury via a tunnel. To the east is the former wharfinger's cottage and attached wharf building (SS 362058).

## TR12 HOLSWORTHY STATION AND RAILWAY VIADUCTS
Holsworthy Hamlets
SS 343035                          ✳
Holsworthy Station survives but the slate-hung station house and offices are in decay. The station was resited when the L&SWR's branch from Okehampton was extended to Bude in 1898. It is approached from the east by a stone viaduct of c1879 (SS 345036) with eight arches, now minus

TR7: Clovelly pier and limekiln *see page 43*
*Photo: Marilyn Palmer*

its parapets. A ten-arched viaduct of 1898 carried the extension to Bude (SS 338035). This was constructed in concrete, made to look like masonry, and was the first such work of this size to be built.

## TR13 HALLSPILL LIMEKILNS
Huntshaw
SS 469235                                              ✳
Two early circular kilns joined together, with round arches to the working areas, by the Torridge.

## TR14 HALLSANNERY LIMEKILN
Landcross
SS 460246                                         ☆ ✳
A striking crenellated kiln with pointed Gothic arches providing access to two pots. There is a railed slipway to the Torridge and a ramp to the rear for charging the kiln. The kiln is best seen from the 'Tarka Trail'.

## TR15 YEO VALE TOLLHOUSE
Littleham
SS 455237                                              ✳
A distinctive L-shaped, two-storey tollhouse (Bideford Trust) with projections at each end, all angles and 'Gothic' windows, some of these false. It is in the fork of the old Bideford-Buckland Brewer road and the road to Littleham.

## TR16 LUNDY GRANITE QUARRIES
Lundy Island
SS 138454                                            NT
✳
In the 1860s, the Lundy Granite Co started quarries with a tramway and incline to a shipping place and built accommodation for workers. This was too remote to be successful. There are interesting survivals.

## TR17 LUNDY LIGHTHOUSES
Lundy Island
SS 132443, SS 131482 and SS 143436                    ✳
The granite tower of the old light of 1819 stands on the top of Lundy at SS 132443. The present lighthouses were built in 1893 nearer sea level at the north-west and south-east points of the island.

## TR18 CLAY WORKS
Merton
SS 514123                                              ☆
Extensive clay works are still in production on Merton Moors, where beds have been worked from pits and mines since the seventeenth century. The clay has provided the raw material for the pale Marland bricks, so common in north Devon. The pits were linked to the rail system by a narrow-gauge railway from 1880 to 1920. A large brick and tile works was dismantled in the 1940s. There are other clay works at Meeth, West Devon.

## TR19 ANNERY KILN LIMEKILNS
Monkleigh
SS 463228                                              ✳
A fine block of kilns and small settlement by the Torridge. The kilns have pointed and round arches and interesting detail in the stonework. There is a ramp to the top from the side nearest the river.

## TR20 BEAM AQUEDUCT
Monkleigh
SS 473209                                              ✳
A five-span masonry aqueduct by James Green which carried Lord Rolle's Torrington Canal over the River Torridge. It is 55 ft (16.8 m) high and 23 ft (7 m) between parapets. The 6-mile (9.7 km) private canal was built in 1824-7 to carry limestone and fuel to kilns along its course. It left the river 2 miles (3.2 km) above Bideford Bridge at Sea Lock and followed the river course to a canal basin below Torrington (TR8). An inclined plane at Landcross (SS 463224) raised the canal above river level. The canal closed in 1871 when the Bideford-Torrington railway was built over part of its course. The aqueduct now carries the drive to Beam House Activity Centre.

## TR21 APPLEDORE QUAY, RICHMOND DOCK AND SHIPYARDS
Appledore, Northam
SS 465305                                          ❑ ✳
Appledore's quay on the Torridge was constructed in 1845, with widening and straightening in 1939 and heightening for flood defence works in 1997. The town is noted for its shipbuilding industry, significant in the eighteenth and nineteenth centuries, and still much in evidence today in its modern covered yard at Bidna (1969). In 1855 William Yeo built Richmond Yard (SS 465304) on the site of Appledore's original quay, for building and launching wooden ships. The yard consists of a stone-lined dry dock 330 ft (100.6 m) long, built to take up to four wooden schooners at any time, and two slips. A further dock, Newquay or Top yard, remains to the south down New Quay Street (SS 465299). The **North Devon Maritime Museum** in Odun Road is an essential visit for those interested in the industrial and maritime history of the area.

## TR22 BIDNA WINDMILL STUMP
Northam
SS 457296                                              ✳
Residual remains of a brick-built tower mill, on a hill crest east of the Bideford-Appledore road. It is thought that the tower was built on the sub-structure of a post mill. Part of a square base and a **45**

TR26: Heanton windmill tower, Petrocstow

small section of the tower remain. The mill was destroyed by a storm in 1919.

## TR23 BUDE CANAL: TAMAR LAKE RESERVOIR AND VIRWORTHY WHARF
Pancrasweek
SS 296108 and SS 298103 ❑
James Green's triangular reservoir and earth dam, now a nature reserve, survive at Tamar Lake with a modern overflow channel. From here, a feeder or aqueduct carries water to Virworthy Wharf where the wharfinger's house remains and a restored storage building has displays inside. After closure, part of the northern branch from Tamar Lake was used to supply water to Bude.

## TR24 BUCKS MILLS LIMEKILNS
Parkham
SS 355236 ✳
This fishing village has remains of two sets of limekilns. Near the beach is a heavily 'consolidated' kiln, with filled pots and hearths. Of greater interest is the rectangular block sited halfway up the cliff. This was linked by an inclined plane to the top of the cliff, but cliff-falls have severed this link and the plane is now detached.

## TR25 POWLER'S PIECE TOLLHOUSE
Parkham
SS 370185 ✳
A small, remote, single-storey stone tollhouse of two bays with central porch, built by the Bideford Trust when the road was constructed in the 1850s.

## TR26 HEANTON WINDMILL TOWER
Petrockstow
SS 491103 ✳
The remains of a squared-rubble stone tower with traces of render survive in a field. A stone from the doorway, now preserved elsewhere, indicates 1756 as a building date.

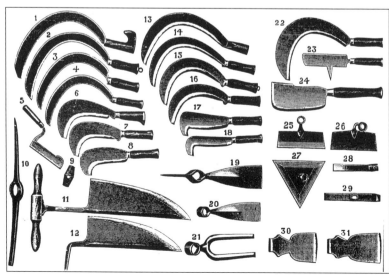

W27: Hand tools made at the Finch Foundry, Sticklepath *see page 53*

West Devon is the district most dominated by Dartmoor, which has its highest point near Okehampton. To the north, centred on Hatherleigh, is an agricultural landscape, while to the west is the once-industrialised Tamar valley. Chagford and Tavistock were stannary towns for Dartmoor's tin industry, but Dartmoor also had granite quarries, a gunpowder mill, peat works and water supplies from leats and reservoirs. The Tamar valley, bordering on Cornwall, had mines for copper, tin, lead, silver and arsenic, and there were smelting works at Weir Quay and limekilns along the tidal river banks. The Tamar was a major waterway inland to Morwellham Quay, served by the Tavistock Canal and Devon Great Consols tramway. Slate was quarried at Mill Hill, around Lifton and South Zeals, and scattered outcrops of limestone quarried for burning. Meldon had aplite and roadstone quarries, the latter still producing railway ballast. Ball clay is worked in the north at Meeth. Industries based on agriculture include corn milling and woollen textiles at Chagford, and dairy products at Lifton and North Tawton. Tavistock had important iron foundries. Early hydro-electric power (HEP) sites were at Okehampton (1889) and Chagford (1891); today, the district has three stations. The Plymouth & Dartmoor Railway served granite quarries and Princetown with its infamous prison. The London & South Western Railway traversed the north of Dartmoor and branches diverged to north Devon and Cornwall. There was a duplication of L&SWR and GWR lines from Lydford Junction through Tavistock to Plymouth.

## W1 CALSTOCK VIADUCT
Bere Ferrers
SX 433686                                     ✳

Impressive 12-arched viaduct across the Tamar, opened in 1908 and still carrying the branch railway from Plymouth via Bere Alston to Gunnislake on the Cornish side. A series of photographs recorded the building of this late viaduct with concrete blocks in 1904-7. A railway trip is recommended.

## W2 TAVY RAILWAY BRIDGE
Bere Ferrers
SX 450615                                     ✳

Long bridge with arched iron spans, opened in 1890 for the Plymouth, Devonport & South Western Junction Railway, giving direct connection between Waterloo and Plymouth. After the main line closed in 1968, this section became the branch to Gunnislake.

## W3 RATTLEBROOK HEAD PEAT WORKS
Bridestowe and Sourton
SX 560871                                     ✳

High up on Dartmoor, at 1740 ft (530 m), is the demolished West of England Compressed Peat Co's works of 1878-80, an attempt to dig and carbonise peat for fuel. The course of a tramway, with a reversal, can be followed. Peat was last dug in the 1950s for horticultural use.

## W4 CHERRY BROOK POWDER MILLS
Dartmoor Forest
SX 628773                                     ✳

A gunpowder mill was built by George Frean in

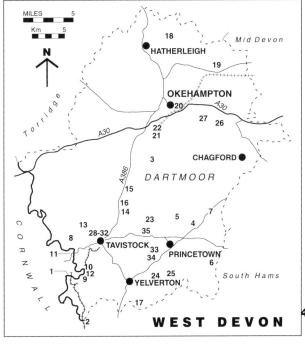

MILES 5
Km 5
N

Mid Devon

18
HATHERLEIGH

19

OKEHAMPTON
20
27  26
22
21

3          CHAGFORD

DARTMOOR

15

16
14       23    5    7
             4
13       35
8  28-32
11        TAVISTOCK 33        PRINCETOWN
10                   34                6
1                              South Hams
12
9       24  25
YELVERTON

17

2

**WEST DEVON**

Torridge

A30

A386

CORNWALL

47

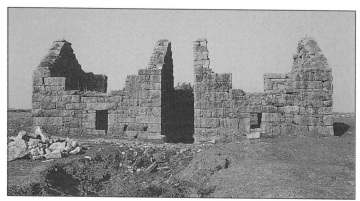

1844-46 at this isolated spot between Two Bridges and Post Bridge, and worked until 1897. Remains include water-powered incorporating mills and two chimneys from the production houses. A row of workers' cottages has been restored and the old school and chapel contains a pottery (SX 628769). Beside the track is a mortar for testing the powder.

## W5 DEVONPORT LEAT
Dartmoor Forest and Walkhampton
SX 608780 (source)                                    ✳
A leat some 28 miles (45 km) from the West Dart, Blackabrook and Cowsic streams, built by the Plymouth Dock Water Co. in 1793-1801 to supply water to Plymouth Dock and Stoke Damerell. The upper part now feeds the Burrator Reservoir. It includes an 1898 aqueduct over the Cowsic (SX 601754), a tunnel at Nun's Cross (SX 606698 to SX 601699), and a cascade down Raddick Hill to an iron aqueduct across the Meavy (SX 573714). The dry course on Roborough Common south of Yelverton follows the older Plymouth Leat, built by Sir Francis Drake in 1589-91 and starved of water by the Burrator reservoir three centuries later.

## W6 HEXWORTHY MINE
Dartmoor Forest
SX 655710                                               ✳
The site includes two earlier mines reopened in 1889-97 and 1905-12 when 197 tons of black tin were produced. There are traces of dressing floors and a leat and aqueduct to a large stone wheelpit at the Henroost site (SX 660711). This was connected by tramway to more extensive dressing floors at Hooten Wheals (SX 655708). The whole area around the O Brook valley has evidence of tin streaming and openworks. Weekford (SX 662724) has a stamping mill and blowing house.

**48**

## W7 POSTBRIDGE
Dartmoor Forest
SX 648789                                               ✳
The most famous and accessible of the Dartmoor clapper bridges, with three spans of large granite slabs laid between stone piers; probably medieval. Such bridges were for pedestrians or packhorses only. Postbridge spans the East Dart beside the Princetown-Moretonhampstead road. Downstream is a ruined clapper alongside Bellever Bridge (by James Green, 1831) at SX 658773.

## W8 DEVON GREAT CONSOLS MINE
Gulworthy
SX 426734                                               ☆
Worked in 1844-1902, this was once the largest copper mine in Europe, producing nearly ³/₄ million tons of ore. The peak year of 1856 saw production of c29,000 tons, at a time when a 4¹/₂-mile (7.2 km) railway was built to Morwellham Quay. Arsenic became increasingly important and over 75,000 tons were produced before the mine closed. At one time the mine had 33 waterwheels and seven steam engines. Much has been demolished and the site forested but the ruins of a 1920s arsenic works and stack stand amid extensive waste tips still free of vegetation. Access to the site is by permission of Tavistock Woodlands. The railway course survives, with its incline down to Morwellham. There are miners' houses at Wheal Josiah and Wheal Maria.

## W9 GAWTON MINE
Gulworthy
SX 452688                                               ☆
Gawton Quay on the River Tamar was an important shipping place which also had lime kilns. Just above was Gawton Mine, which yielded 20,429 tons of copper ore and 16,487 tons of arsenic from the second half of the nineteenth century to 1902.

Traces of this industry include arsenic calciners, a refinery house, and an engine house linked to twin crushing and grinding houses. A long flue for removing poisonous arsenic fumes leads to a tall leaning stack (SX 456689) above the valley.

## W10 MORWELLHAM QUAY
Gulworthy
SX 446697 ❑

Once a major copper ore shipping port on the Tamar, connected by inclined planes to the Tavistock Canal and Devon Great Consols railway. Long abandoned, it has been restored to its appearance in the 1860s with staff in period costume recreating the atmosphere, including an assayer, blacksmith and cooper. There are tiled ore floors around the dock of 1858, tramways, limekilns, waterwheels (one for crushing manganese ore), workers' cottages and a museum. A tramway takes visitors into the George and Charlotte copper mine. Also here is the 640-kW Morwellham HEP station with two Turgo-turbines which opened in 1934 and takes water from the Tavistock Canal. Above Morwellham is the canal terminus and the west portal of the Morwell Down tunnel.

## W11 NEW BRIDGE
Gulworthy
SX 433722 ✳

Major border crossing for the A390 into Cornwall, a fine granite bridge of c1520. There is a small tollhouse on the Devon side. This was the lowest bridging point of the Tamar until the Tamar Bridge was opened from Plymouth to Saltash in 1961. Two other good stone bridges are at Horsebridge (SX 400749) and Greystone Bridge (SX 369803), both dating from the 1430s.

## W12 NEW QUAY
Gulworthy
SX 454695 ☆

Just downstream from Morwellham, with ruined cottages and three limekilns, the earliest said to date from 1774 and last worked in 1914. A waterwheel drew small limestone wagons to the top via a short inclined plane. New Quay developed as an overspill to Morwellham when mineral exports were rising.

## W13 MILL HILL QUARRIES AND CANAL
Lamerton
SX 452748 ✳

Large slate quarries, now being re-worked, were important in the eighteenth century and after 1819 when a 1½-mile (2.4 km) branch of the Tavistock Canal reached here. A horse tramway alongside

W10: Morwellham Quay    *Photo: Michael Atkinson*

replaced the canal in 1846-60. At Mill Hill, are workers' cottages (1850s), an old chapel and warehouse (both converted to houses). Part of the canal's course and a bridge are at Middle Lumburn Bridge (SX 454743). The best section, although dry, can be followed from the A390 to the Tavistock Canal junction at SX 462726.

## W14 MARY TAVY HYDRO-ELECTRIC STATION
Mary Tavy
SX 509785 ◼

England's largest HEP station began in 1932 when the West Devon Mining & Power Co brought water from Hillbridge Weir on the Tavy to a reservoir above the site. No.1 station has three 220 kW Francis turbines. No.2 station, with three 650 kW Pelton

W14: Interior, Mary Tavy HEP station
*Photo: National Power*

W15: Wheal Betsy engine house, Mary Tavy

turbines, was opened in 1937, using water from Tavy Cleave via the 4¹/₂-mile (7.2 km) Reddaford Leat to the Wheal Jewell Reservoir. Diesel generators were used in 1934-75 to supplement the turbines during water shortages.

## W15 WHEAL BETSY
Mary Tavy
SX 510814                                      NT ✳
A landmark pumping engine house just below the A386 across the edge of Dartmoor. The mine was active for lead, silver and zinc in the nineteenth century and a 50-inch pumping engine worked here in 1868-77.

## W16 WHEAL FRIENDSHIP
Mary Tavy
SX 506795                                      ✳ ☆
A copper mine, developed from 1798 onwards by the famous mining engineer John Taylor. It was reworked for arsenic from the late nineteenth century until 1925, and ruins of the arsenic plant are visible from a footpath. Hordon (SX 521801) has mineworkers' cottages and a small disused chapel of 1860.

W17: Dewerstone incline winding drum

## W17 DEWERSTONE QUARRIES AND TRAMWAY
Meavy
SX 537641                                      NT ✳
Four small granite quarries on the wooded spur between the Plym and Meavy rivers have the course of a tramway on two levels, connected by a 1,120-ft (341 m) incline with stone sleeper blocks and the remains of a winding drum and stone housing. Active in 1858, the tramway was never joined to the Tavistock railway as intended.

## W18 MONKOKEHAMPTON MILL
Monkokehampton
SS 580053                                      ✳ ■
A leat takes water from the River Okement to this nineteenth-century stone and brick corn mill, still worked occasionally by the local farmer for grinding animal feed. Of two waterwheels, that in working order is an overshot by Garnish and Lemon of Barnstaple.

## W19 NORTH TAWTON WOOLLEN MILL
North Tawton
SS 657016                                      ☆ ■
Last used for wool grading, this derelict site includes a long four-storey range beside the Taw and an extensive group of north-light sheds. There is a row of workers' houses. In complete contrast, the ultra-modern Taw Valley Creamery overlooks North Tawton from the west.

## W20 TOWN MILL
Okehampton
SX 590949                                      ✳
The Town Mill, converted to a house, has a turning waterwheel of 1882 by J Luxton & Co of Hatherleigh. The **Museum of Dartmoor Life** in George Street (SX 588951) has a 16 ft (4.9 m) iron wheel, salvaged from Combe Park Farm on the Roadford reservoir site in 1986.

## W21 MELDON QUARRIES
Okehampton Hamlets
SX 564922                                    ✳
The Meldon viaduct dominates the valley, which has evidence for mining and quarrying. The flooded Meldon Pool (SX 564922) was a limestone quarry, once pumped dry by two waterwheels placed across the river. There is a limekiln here, and an earlier one opposite. There was also a tramway in the valley and a mine adit is beside the footpath. To the south-east are disused quarries for aplite (SX 566920), a raw material for attempted glass-works in the 1890s and 1920s. The large Meldon Quarry (SX 568925), active for railway ballast and roadstone, was first opened c1895.

## W22 MELDON VIADUCT
Okehampton Hamlets
SX 565923                                    ✳
This iron lattice-girder viaduct is 144 ft (44 m) high with six spans across the West Okement valley just below the Meldon Reservoir, and was opened as two parts in 1874 (wrought iron) and 1878 (steel). Designed by W R Galbraith for the London & South Western Railway, it is the last survivor of its type in England. Trains for Meldon Quarry still use the via-duct as a siding.

## W23 MERRIVALE BLOWING HOUSE
Peter Tavy
SX 552766                                    ✳
A ruined blowing house, on the west side of the Walkham River above Merrivale Bridge, has seen recent important excavations. Two other sites, east of the river, are at SX 553754 and 553762. Difficult to date precisely, such small structures were for smelt-ing tin won from streamworks, with water-powered bellows working the furnace. The wheelpit and granite mould stones may survive. Other examples can be found in many Dartmoor valleys.

W19: North Tawton woollen mill from the air
*Photo: RCHME © Crown Copyright*

W22: Meldon Viaduct

## W24 BURRATOR RESERVOIR
Sheepstor
SX 552680                                    ✳
Surrounded by rocky tors and forest, this is an at-tractive reservoir. A granite dam with a concrete core was built across the Burrator gorge in 1893-8 for Plymouth's water supply, with an earth dam at SX 557679. Both were heightened 10 ft (3 m) in 1928 to increase the reservoir's capacity.

## W25 EYLESBARROW MINE
Sheepstor
SX 598682                                    ✳
A tin mine was recorded here in 1671, but most evidence survives from the early nineteenth cen-tury. There are traces of six stamping floors and two wheelpits with lines of stones for supporting flat rods at SX594680 and SX 592682. Large stones at SX 5926576 mark a blast furnace and reverbera-tory furnace. This was Dartmoor's last smelting house and probably the last tin blast furnace in Devon. Walter Wellington was recorded here, pro-ducing 276 tons of tin in 1822-31.

## W26 RAMSLEY MINE
South Tawton
SX 651930                                    ✳**51**
A copper mine, worked c1850-80 and the early

W24: The dam at Burrator Reservoir

twentieth century. There are large iron-stained waste tips on the valley side. A landmark chimney of 1900 was felled by lightning in January 1998. Nearby is the foundation of a horizontal winding engine.

## W27 FINCH FOUNDRY
Sticklepath
SX 642941

NT ✳

Former corn and cloth mills became an edge-tool factory in 1814. It was worked by Finch Brothers until 1960, manufacturing agricultural tools such as billhooks, scythes and shovels. Three waterwheels (two by Pearce of Tavistock) drove a pair of tilt-hammers, drop-forging hammers, a metal-cutting shears, a fan for the forges, a grindstone for sharpening tools and a polishing wheel. The foundry has been restored.

## W28 BEDFORD SQUARE AND HOUSES
Tavistock
SX 482744 ✳
Impressive square with town hall in local green

Hurdwick stone, market hall and statue of the 7th Duke of Bedford. Workers' houses were erected in the 1850s and 60s by the Bedfords on mining royalties, notably at West Bridge (SX 477736), Fitzford (SX 475738) and Parkwood Road (SX 486746).

## W29 LAUNCESTON ROAD TOLLHOUSE
Tavistock
SX 473747 ✳
Two-storey slate hung tollhouse of the Tavistock Trust, octagonal with a central chimney, placed at a fork in the Old and New roads, the latter being built to lessen the effect of a steep descent into the town. Other tollhouses are on the Okehampton and Princetown Roads.

## W30 TAVISTOCK CANAL
Tavistock to Gulworthy
SX 480742 to SX 444701 ✳
A 4-mile (6.4 km) canal, built in 1803-17 by the mining engineer John Taylor. It includes warehouses at Tavistock's Canal Wharf (SX 480742), the Lumburn embankment and aqueduct (SX 462726), a branch to Mill Hill, an ambitious 1½-mile (2.4 km) tunnel under Morwell Down (SX 461723 to SX 449703) with portals inscribed '1803', and an inclined plane descending 233 ft (71 m) to Morwellham Quay. The canal carried copper ores, granite, coal and limestone until 1873. It now provides water for the Morwellham HEP station.

## W31 TAVISTOCK IRONWORKS
Parkwood Road, Tavistock
SX 486747 ✳
Stone buildings of this important foundry survive in good order. Formerly Gill & Rundle's foundry, it was taken over in 1868 by rivals Nicholls Williams of the Bedford Foundry in Bannawell Street. Steam en-

W27: Tilt hammers at the Finch Foundry, Sticklepath
*Photo: National Trust*

W30: Tavistock Canal wharf

gines for mines were manufactured here. It later became a wool combing mill until 1965, and is now occupied by Kaminskis house and garden centre.

## W32 TAVISTOCK VIADUCT
Tavistock
SX 480746                                              ✳
Dominant eight-arched granite viaduct with one thicker pier, opened in 1890 by the Plymouth, Devonport & South Western Junction Railway. Since closure in 1968, the viaduct is now a footpath providing an excellent view over the town. Part of Tavistock North station remains in a housing development. A second viaduct is at Wilminstone (SX 491755).

## W33 FOGGINTOR AND SWELL TOR QUARRIES
Walkhampton
SX 560733 and SX 567735                                ✳
Large granite quarries opened with the Plymouth & Dartmoor Railway in the 1820s. Foggintor provided granite for Nelson's Column. It closed c1900, leaving crane bases within and a large waste tip outside. A ruined hamlet for workers and their families includes a blacksmiths shop and school. Over the hill, with traces of an incline and branches, Swell Tor Quarries (SX 560733) worked until the 1930s. There are ruins of the dressing area, smithy, magazine and abandoned stones including large corbels destined for widening London Bridge in 1901.

## W34 PLYMOUTH AND DARTMOOR RAILWAY
Walkhampton
SX 565726                                              ✳
Opened by Sir Thomas Tyrwhitt in 1823 to develop the western edge of Dartmoor, carrying farm products, peat and granite, but only the last became important. The full 24 miles (38.4 km) of this 4 ft 6 in (1.37 m) gauge line opened in 1826 to

W30: Lamburn aqueduct, Tavistock Canal

Princetown. The upper section was relaid at standard gauge as the Princetown Railway (1883-1956) from Yelverton. The ascending line curves around Kings Tor, with sidings to Criptor, Foggintor and Swell Tor quarries; a bridge and embankment have been by-passed by the newer line at Yes Tor Bottom (SX 565726). At Clearbrook further south, is an old warehouse or 'wharf' beside the line (SX 517651).

## W35 MERRIVALE QUARRY
Whitchurch
SX 546753                                              ✳
The last active Dartmoor granite quarry closed in 1997. A waste tip of big angular blocks typical of dimension stone quarries spills down to the road at Merrivale Bridge. Started in 1876 as Tor Quarry by William Duke, it supplied granite to Tower Bridge, West Hartlepool Docks, New Scotland Yard, New London Bridge, the Old Bailey and the Falklands War Memorial, Port Stanley. Evidence for stone-cutting can be seen above on the slopes of Great Staple Tor.

Acworth, R — The Anthracite Seams of North Devon', *Journal Trevithick Society*, No.18, 1991, 117-125

Adams, B & Thomas, A — *A Potworks in Devonshire: the history and products of the Bovey Tracey Potteries, 1750-1836,* Sayce Publishing, 1996

Atkinson, M, Burt, R, & Waite, P — *Dartmoor Mines: the mines of the granite mass,* Exeter IA Group, 2nd ed. 1983

Atkinson, M (ed.) — *Exmoor's Industrial Archaeology,* Exmoor Books, 1997

Binding, J — *Brunel's Royal Albert Bridge,* Twelveheads Press, 1997

Bone, M — *Barnstaple's Industrial Archaeology: a guide,* Exeter IA Group, 1975

Booker, F — *Industrial Archaeology of the Tamar Valley,* David & Charles, 1967

Booker, F — *The Story of Morwellham,* Dartington Amenity Research Trust, 1970

Born, A — 'Blue Slate Quarrying in South Devon: an Ancient Industry', *Industrial Archaeology Review,* XI, No.1, 1988, 51-67

Chitty, M — *Industrial Archaeology of Exeter: a guide,* Exeter IA Group, 2nd ed.1974

Christy, P & Gahan, D — *Barnstaple's Vanished Lace Industry,* Edward Gaskell, 1997

Cleaver, D et al — *Bideford Black: the history of a unique local industry,* Sound Archives North Devon, 1994

Clew, K — *The Exeter Canal,* Phillimore, 1984

Ewans, M C — *The Haytor Granite Tramway and Stover Canal,* David & Charles, 1964

Gaskell Brown, C (ed.) — *A Guide to the Industrial Archaeology of Plymouth and Millbrook, Cornwall,* W.E.A., 2nd ed. 1980

George, B — *James Green: canal builder and county surveyor (1781-1849),* Devon Books, 1997

Hadfield, C — *The Canals of South West England,* David & Charles, 1967

Hall, J — *Railway Landmarks in Devon,* David & Charles, 1982

Hamilton Jenkin, A K — *Mines of Devon: the southern area,* David & Charles, 1974

Hamilton Jenkin, A K — *Mines of Devon: north and east of Dartmoor,* Devon Library Services, 1981

Harris, H — *Industrial Archaeology of Dartmoor,* David & Charles, 1968 4th ed. 1992 Peninsula Press, Newton Abbot

Harris, H — *The Grand Western Canal,* David & Charles, 1973

Harris, H & Ellis, M — *The Bude Canal,* David & Charles, 1972

Havinden, M — 'Lime as a means of agricultural improvement: the Devon example', in Chalkin, C. & Havinden, M. *Rural Change & Urban Growth 1500-1800,* Longman, 1974

Hawkings, D J — *Water from the Moor: An illustrated history of the Plymouth, Stonehouse and Devonport Leats,* Devon Books, 1987

Hedges, C — *The Tavistock Canal,* Dartington Amenity Research Trust, 1975

Henderson, C — 'The Archaeology of Exeter Quay', *Devon Archaeology,* IV, 1991, 1-15

Kanefsky, J — *Devon Tollhouses,* Exeter IA Group, 2nd ed.1984

| | |
|---|---|
| Messenger, M J | *North Devon Clay*, Twelveheads Press, 1982 |
| Minchinton, W | *Industrial Archaeology in Devon*, Dartington Amenity Research Trust, 1968, 2nd ed. 1973, 3rd edition 1976 |
| Minchinton, W | *Devon's Industrial Past: a guide*, Dartington Amenity Research Trust, 1986 |
| Minchinton, W | *Windmills of Devon*, Exeter IA Group, 1977 |
| Minchinton, W | *Devon at Work: Past and Present*, David & Charles, 1974 |
| Minchinton, W | *Life to the City: an illustrated history of Exeter's water supply from the Romans to the present day*, Devon Books, 1987 |
| Minchinton, W & Perkins, J | *Tidemills of Devon and Cornwall*, Exeter IA Group, 1971 |
| Newman, P (ed.) | *Mining and Metallurgy in South-West Britain*, Peak District Mines Historical Soc. & Historical Metallurgy Soc., 1996 |
| Newman, P | *A Field Guide to the Dartmoor Tin Industry*, Chercombe Press, 1998 |
| Otter, R (ed.) | *Civil Engineering Heritage: Southern England*, Thomas Telford, 1994 |
| Parkhouse, N | 'Building Calstock Viaduct', *Archive*, 2, 1994, 33-54 |
| Patrick, A | *The Growth and Decline of Morwellham*, Dartington Amenity Research Trust, 1975 |
| Phillips, C & Wilson, R | 'Watermills in East Devon', *Devon & Cornwall Notes & Queries*, 1974-80, 33-34 |
| Pye, A & Weddell, P | 'A Survey of the Gawton Mine & Arsenic Works, Tavistock Hamlets, West Devon', *Industrial Archaeology Review*, XV, No.1, 1992, 62-96 |
| Richardson, I & Watts, M | 'Finch Foundry, Devon', *Industrial Archaeology Review*, XVIII, No.1, 1995, 83-95 |
| Rolt, L T C | *The Potters Field*, David & Charles, 1974 |
| Spooner, G (ed.) | *Worth's Dartmoor*, David & Charles, 1967 |
| Stanier, P | 'The Granite Quarrying Industry in Devon and Cornwall: Part One 1800-1910', *Industrial Archaeology Review*, VII, No.2, 1985, 171-189 |
| Stanier, P | 'The Granite Quarrying Industry in Devon and Cornwall: Part Two 1910-1985', *Industrial Archaeology Review*, IX, No.1, 1986, 7-13 |
| Strong, H | *Industries of North Devon*, 1889, rev. ed. David & Charles, 1971 |
| Thomas, D | *A Regional History of the Railways of Great Britain, Vol. 1, The West Country*, David & Charles, 5th ed., 1981 |
| Thorpe, J (ed.) | *North Devon Watermills*, North Devon Archaeological Society, 1989 |
| Varley, D | 'John Heathcoat (1783-1861): founder of the machine-made lace industry', *Textile History*, I, 1968, 41-45 |
| Wade, E A | *The Redlake Tramway and china clay works*, Twelveheads Press, 1982 |
| Watts, M | 'Farm and Threshing Mill at Poltimore Farm, Farway, Devon', *Industrial Archaeology Review*, XIII, No.2, 1991, 182-189 |

TE17: Two views of the granite pointwork on the Haytor Tramway

*Photos: Marilyn Palmer*

## ACKNOWLEDGEMENTS

The authors are grateful to the many people who have helped in the production of this book in various ways, but especially Michael Atkinson, Ann Bone, Anne Born, Brian Brett, Felicity Cole, Charles Crichton, Chris Henderson, Marilyn Palmer, Reg Shield, Alan Stoyel, Martin and Sue Watts, and staff of the National Trust, the Westcountry Studies Library, Exeter, and Devonport Management Plc.

Photographs are acknowledged in the text. All others are from the authors' collections.

Maps are based on 1996 Automobile Association mapping.

## THE AUTHORS

MIKE BONE wrote *Barnstaple's Industrial Archaeology* (1975) and is editor of the *Bristol Industrial Archaeological Society Journal*. PETER STANIER edits the AIA's *Industrial Archaeology News*. His publications include the *Shire Guide to Devon* (1989) and *Mines of Cornwall and Devon* (1998)

## ASSOCIATION FOR INDUSTRIAL ARCHAEOLOGY

This book is being published to mark the AIA's 1998 Conference at Seale Hayne, Newton Abbot. The AIA was established in 1973 to promote the study of industrial archaeology and encourage improved standards of recording, research, conservation and publication. It aims to support individuals and groups involved in the study and recording of past industrial activity and the preservation of industrial monuments, to represent the interests of industrial archaeology at national level, to hold conferences and seminars, and to publish the results of research. The Association is a voluntary one. It publishes the *Industrial Archaeology Review* which is sent twice yearly to all members, who also receive the quarterly *Industrial Archaeology News*. Further details may be obtained from the AIA Liaison Officer, AIA Office, c/o School of Archaeological Studies, University of Leicester, Leicester LE1 7RH.

COVER ILLUSTRATIONS: *Main illustration:* The Beam Aqueduct on the Rolle Canal, from the engraving by Thomas Allom, 1830 (**TR20**); *inset photo front cover:* Coldharbour Mill, Uffculme (**M16**)

**56** *inset photos, back cover, clockwise from top left:* Torpoint Ferry from a postcard, c1900 (**P17**); A typical Devon milestone; The clapper bridge, Postbridge (**W7**); Devonport Memorial and the Town Hall (**P4**)